SUPP
THE WEAK

By
Samuel Pfeifer M.D.

Translated by
Michael Jobling

SUPPORTING THE WEAK

Copyright © 1994 by Samuel Pfeifer.

Published in Great Britain by Nelson Word Ltd., Milton Keynes, England, 1994.

All rights reserved.

No part of this publication may be reproduced or transmitted in any form or by any means, electronic or mechanical, including photocopy, recording or any information storage or retrieval system, without permission in writing from the publisher.

ISBN 0-85009-599-9   (Australia ISBN 1-86258-296-3)

Unless otherwise indicated in the notes, scripture quotations are directly translated, either from the German or from the New Testament Greek original.

Other quotations are from the following sources:

The Good News Bible, copyright © 1976 by the American Bible Society, New York.

The Revised Standard Version, copyright © 1971 by Division of Christian Education of the National Council of Churches of Christ in the United States of America.

The Everyday Bible—New Century Version, copyright © 1987, 1988 by Word Publishing.

The New International Version, copyright © 1973, 1978, 1984 by International Bible Society.

Reproduced, printed and bound in Great Britain for Nelson Word Ltd. by Cox and Wyman Ltd., Reading.

94 95 96 97 / 10 9 8 7 6 5 4 3 2 1

SUPPORTING THE WEAK

By
Samuel Pfeifer M.D.

WORD PUBLISHING
Nelson Word Ltd
Milton Keynes, England
WORD AUSTRALIA
Kilsyth, Australia
WORD COMMUNICATIONS LTD
Vancouver, B.C., Canada
STRUIK CHRISTIAN BOOKS (PTY) LTD
Cape Town, South Africa
JOINT DISTRIBUTORS SINGAPORE –
ALBY COMMERCIAL ENTERPRISES PTE LTD
and
CAMPUS CRUSADE, ASIA LTD
PHILIPPINE CAMPUS CRUSADE FOR CHRIST
Quezon City, Philippines
CHRISTIAN MARKETING NEW ZEALAND LTD
Havelock North, New Zealand
JENSCO LTD
Hong Kong
SALVATION BOOK CENTRE
Malaysia

To my Father,
who awoke in me an interest
in psychiatry, and a love for
those who are weak.

Contents

Introduction   7

I   PSYCHIATRY IN FLUX
    1. Psychiatry under fire   15
    2. The image of human nature in psychotherapy   29
    3. The miracle of the human brain   41
    4. How mental illness comes about   55

II SUFFERING SOULS
    5. Neurotic disorders - an overview   73
    6. Anxiety, obsessive - compulsive disorders   85
        and the hysterical personality.
    7. Depression, an overview   99
    8. The therapy and pastoral care of severe   123
        depression.
    9. Schizophrenia, an overview   139
    10. Schizophrenia - therapy and pastoral care   155

III HELPING THE WEAK
    11. Schizophrenia: Therapy and Pastoral Care   165
    12. Integrated care for the mentally ill   179
    13. Living with limitations   195

Notes.   209
Bibliography.   229
Index.   243

In the poor
            weak
            sick
            perplexed
            helpless
            defenceless
      the failures
      the dejected
      the doubting
and the doubted
      the wreckers
and the wrecked
people others avoid
            who don't look normal
            who have lost the will to fight on
God arranges to meet us.

—Anton Kerr

Introduction

This book developed from a series of seminars I used to hold on the theme: 'Psychiatry and pastoral care'. The interest these lectures aroused made it clear to me that there are many people looking for answers within the tension between mental illness and spiritual salvation.

Nowadays, psychiatric illness is more problematic than ever before. Depressive disorders in particular, are diagnosed much more frequently. Professor Paul Kielholz, a well-known researcher in this field, writes 'These increases can be traced back to improved diagnosis and treatment of depressive conditions on the one hand, and on the other, its causes lie in the fragmentation and isolation people experience in our throwaway consumer society.'[1]

Hufeland, a German doctor, makes a similar observation. He writes:'Nervous illnesses were never so common as today, never so manifold.'[2] However, the date of this note is somewhat surprising. He wrote this complaint in 1812! In fact, extensive research [3] has shown the risk of developing serious psychological disorder has *not* increased in recent years.[4]

What has increased however, is the awareness of the problem. People talk much more openly about psychological illness nowadays. The opening up of psychiatry means that the average person is much more likely to be confronted with mentally handicapped people. In our highly technical, prosperous society, it is much harder for them to find suitable employment and acceptance within a community than would have been the case years ago among a rural and agricultural population. *The availability of therapy has also increased,*[5] together with a tendency to regard every deviation and emotional disturbance as psychological illness. Yesterday's 'oppressed' are today's 'depressives'.

At first sight pastoral care and psychiatry would seem to be mutually exclusive. Many people take a suspicious view of psychiatry as a science and as a 'system', and with good reason. Only recently Professor Hans Küng made an interesting and justified[6] observation about 'the repression of religion by psychiatry'. Through talking to doctors, theologians and lay people, both Christian and agnostic, I have observed four basic approaches people use to describe this tension:

1. *Psychiatry and religion have nothing to do with each other.* Psychiatric problems are to be solved with the help of psychotherapy and psychiatry. Questions about faith can be left to the church.

2. *Psychological illness is caused, or at any rate made worse, by religion.* People often bring into the argument at this point concepts such as 'religious neurosis' and 'religious mania'. In the process they often disregard the important distinction between the *cause* of a neurosis or mania, and its *expression*. The fact is that the more society is estranged from religion and the church, the less religious content is found in schizophrenia and depressive delusions.[7] Nowadays, people don't rebel against God, they rebel against the demands of society. The basic problem is the same, only the vocabulary has changed.

3. At the other extreme there are those who say (this time from a Christian viewpoint) that *mental illness is a spiritual problem which can only be healed through faith.* Its causes lie for example in lack of holiness, demonic influence, or that a person has not fully grasped the meaning of the cross, and

repented. This approach has adverse spiritual and psychological effects on people who are plagued with mental illness. Such exhortations put them under pressure. They feel that they are excluded from the community of faith. Such an attitude, unbiblical as it is, leads to increased inner tension which can make a psychological illness worse.

All three views are one-sided, and unfair to the mentally ill. For this reason I would like to propose a fourth view as follows:

4. *Psychological disorders are part of our life on earth. It is legitimate to use the biblical idea of 'weakness' in connection with this kind of problem. The Christian community has an important responsibility to fulfil, both in helping to prevent mental disturbances, and in caring for psychologically weak people. It is possible for Christians to work together with psychiatrists, and the co-operation can be of significant help, when both pastoral counsellors and psychiatrists know their limitations, and treat one another with respect.*

Naturally, many of the assertions made in this book are the outcome of experiences I underwent during my training to become a specialist in psychiatry and psychotherapy. I can still remember my first impression of a psychiatric clinic. As a young registrar, I remember well the peculiar feeling of inner tension when I entered, for the first time, a psychiatric admission ward for men. The large room looked like a strange mixture of a shelter for the homeless and a railway station waiting room (it has long since been renovated). The men whom I met there seemed strange, almost sinister. But the more I got to know them, the more I realised that behind their odd exterior, my patients were 'people like you

or I' . . : simply people in a crisis, who happened to need a
stay in the clinic. Eugene Bleuler once wrote, strikingly, that
the basic symptom of psychosis was that 'schizophrenics held
on to their sanity. They do not lose it, it merely becomes
hidden'.[8] In later years it became a fulfilling vocation for me
to accompany sick people along the road where they would
rediscover the healthy part of themselves.

However, the foundations of my present vocation were
laid long before my medical training. My father, who himself
was active for many years as a chaplain in a large rehabilitation clinic, gave me an important stimulus in that direction.
He awoke in me a love for psychologically weak people, and
encouraged my interest in a medical and scientific approach to
psychiatry. The Christianity which I learned at home was a
liberating and enriching experience. For my parents, the
Bible was the guide for living a fulfilled life, and prayer
meant talking naturally with God. I too have personally
experienced the supporting power of a living faith in Christ.

An additional help was a year of integrative studies in
psychology and theology in California. Here I got to know
professors who were academically, as well as biblically well-
grounded, so that they were well-equipped to tackle pressing
questions about the nature of man and the problems of the
human race. They gave me the courage to occupy myself
with psychology, psychotherapy and psychiatry, and to
challenge the world view of these disciplines with critical
questions from a biblical perspective.

In my search for answers, I have found it painful to
discover that most books about pastoral care only address
themselves to minor problems, and give little help towards
gaining a full understanding of schizophrenia and endogenous
depression, of major neuroses or organic brain disorders.[9] On
the other hand, I have also found little advice in psychiatric
literature about dealing with those with psychiatric illness for
whom faith plays an important role. Religious experience is
only described in its pathological manifestations without
adequately underlining its positive aspects.[10]

As professor Küng writes: 'the person who has not understood religion will never understand those great spiritual resources which can act decisively for the good of the patient. He is poorer than those who prescribe treatment with a perception which has been liberated and healed through religious experience.'[10]

New treatments in psychiatry have now made it possible for many people to live outside hospital, but they still have to contend with psychological disabilities which make their life difficult. Not infrequently, pastoral workers and interested Christians come into contact with their suffering. Even though mentally ill people are often immediately attracted to the Christian message of redemption and forgiveness, of love and acceptance from God, and of Christian fellowship, they do not often decide for Christ in the midst of their crisis. Counselling with mentally suffering and weak persons raises many questions. If Christians want to effectively help people with psychiatric disorders, they need to gain a broader understanding of mental illnesses, how they affect people in general, and in particular how they affect people's faith. They need to learn both the possibilities and the limitations of psychiatry and of pastoral care.

This book is intended for those whose search is not just for specialist medical knowledge, but who want to understand the problems of psychological weakness against the background of Christian faith. For this reason, I have intentionally used everyday language. It is a book for pastoral workers and interested lay people, as well as the relatives of the mentally ill.

For those who want to know more about modern psychiatry, I have included a list of recommended literature at the end of the book. Although some illnesses are described in great detail, this book is not intended to replace the physician's expertise.

I am well aware of the limitations of my undertaking. What is being described in the following chapters, is not a new truth, but a description of old experiences set against the background of new discoveries in psychiatry. I write as a doctor, not a theologian, but nevertheless I have tried to combine the discoveries of academic psychiatry with a biblical outlook. There are many matters which I have only been able to touch on briefly, and final answers are often not possible, but in spite of this, I hope to provide the reader with a new understanding of psychologically weak people. As I describe these serious conditions, I hope also to provide a new insight into the Bible.

If a by-product of this book is to stimulate increased dialogue between Christian pastoral counsellors and doctors, between practical theology and clinical psychiatry, and if it gives pastoral counsellors and lay helpers the courage to help the weak, it will have fulfilled its purpose.

—Dr Samuel Pfeifer

Translator's Notes

It has been a privilege to translate Dr. Pfeifer's book. In so doing I have tried to keep as near as possible to the wording of the German text while expressing the thoughts in a way which would sound natural to an English ear.

Two German words have caused me difficulty throughout the book. The words 'Seelsorge' and 'Seelsorger' (literally, 'soul-care' and 'soul-carer') do not have exact equivalents in English. The word, 'Counselling' is too secular and should be non-directive, 'pastoral work' is too practical, and a 'Pastor' has to be the leader of a congregation as well as giving personal care to members of the flock. In most cases I have used the rather cumbersome phrases 'pastoral counselling' and 'pastoral counsellor'. By 'pastoral counsellor' should be understood any person, lay or ordained, professional or amateur, who is engaged in caring for the spiritual and mental welfare of others within a Christian context and framework of understanding.

—Michael Jobling

PART 1

PSYCHIATRY
IN FLUX

CHAPTER 1

PSYCHIATRY UNDER FIRE

*I*t is doubtful if any department of medicine raises more questions than psychiatry. Many people have 'hang-ups' about associating with people who are mentally ill. Someone wrote to me: 'I have difficulty in meeting people like that. They are so strange . . . a bit frightening at times. And I'm not so sure about psychology and psychiatry. I don't believe there are any real 'experts', in any case, ordinary help from other people is what is needed more than anything else.' In the course of private conversations about psychiatry, I often encounter fear and defensive resistance, or criticism and prejudice.

Yet we are continually being confronted by psychiatric problems. Depression and psychosomatic disturbances trouble modern people more than ever. Every second person has a near relative who has already required at least one period of treatment in a psychiatric hospital.[1]

Even Christians Have Problems

No doubt, Christians are not immune to psychiatric illness. This may be a shocking statement to some. Yet Christians are just as prone to weakness and temptation as anyone else. Again and again I hear people ask: 'How can a Bible-believing Christian make sense of the existence of mental illness?'

What causes:

- a thirty-year-old lady to be so afraid of the next day that she cannot cope without tranquillisers?
- a forty-five-year-old man, who sustained a head injury in a road traffic accident to suffer with bursts of anger in which on one occasion he smashed a television set to pieces?
- a forty-year-old married woman to fall into such a deep depression that she can no longer sleep properly and to develop deep doubts about her faith, which was formerly a great strength to her?
- a twenty-two-year-old student to gradually come to feel that his fellow students are persecuting him, to start saying strange things, and to violently attack his father?

Do Christians really have any explanation for these conditions? Is it possible to develop from the Bible models which can help us understand such people, and at the same time be true to reality? Or do you have to entrust yourself to a school of psychotherapy to understand mentally ill people? Is there a biblical view of human behaviour, which not only explains sin, but can also be applied to serious mental illness?

Illness or Problems?

If certain psychiatrists and their books are to be believed, practically everyone is psychologically disturbed and in need of treatment. All too often no distinction is made any longer between minor and major conditions. Many experts are warning that nowadays our understanding of 'illness' has been stretched too far. We are well on the way to the 'therapeutic society'[2] which exists in America,[3] where people expect not to be able to exist without counselling. This kind of psychologising of our society is questioned, not only in Christian circles, but also by other eminently responsible authors who understand the limitations of psychology and its therapeutic methods.[4]

Nevertheless, it is beyond dispute that the incidence of depressive conditions has increased markedly in recent years. many people suffer as a result of emotional wounds in early childhood as well as traumatic experiences in later life.

The worries people had in earlier generations about issues of sheer survival have subsided. It is a distinctive feature of our affluent society that inner conflicts and psychosomatic complaints have become more central to its life, and anyone who doesn't feel content with their environment will feel themselves psychologically disturbed. We often forget, moreover, that internal tensions, anxieties, and emotional ups and downs are part of life and can come to the surface at times of disappointment or crisis. They do not necessarily indicate the presence of an illness (in any case, not one which merits specialist treatment).

Severe Psychiatric Disorders

The excessive use of psychiatric terminology in pop psychology conceals the reality that there are psychiatric illnesses which go beyond the everyday problems of life and call for special treatment by a medical psychiatrist. This applies to the disorders in the list that follows, all of which in their restricted definitions are included among the psychiatric illnesses and affect between five and ten per cent of the population:

Schizophrenia, and other psychoses
Endogenous depression
Organic brain disease (especially resulting from brain damage, or in old age)
Severe neuroses

The risk of becoming ill with schizophrenia once during your life stands at about one per cent, the risk of a severe

depression at about ten per cent. About five per cent of the
population suffers from disability as a result of a severe
psychiatric illness. About fifteen per cent are affected by a
moderately severe disorder (neuroses, personality disorders
and substance dependencies). A further twenty per cent
undergo minor and temporary difficulties.[5]

It is not always possible to draw a sharp distinction
between minor and major conditions. The course of many
psychiatric disorders follows a wave pattern. A ripple of
personal unease can rise to the flood tide of a major
breakdown under the influence of a storm of internal distress
or external difficulty. A disorder may seem dramatic at a
given moment, but that implies nothing about its long-term
development. The psychiatrist will often find impressive
improvements taking place even after a severe breakdown.

In this book I want to give priority to the consideration of
severe illness where the long term prognosis involves major
suffering and obvious restrictions to everyday life. Talking it
through is of only limited use in dealing with these conditions,
and not helpful at all in some phases of the illness, because
the people affected are not fully receptive to encouragement.
Pastoral counselling and psychotherapy both come to the
limitations of their usefulness at this point. Any treatment
which did not draw on the help of specialist psychiatric
knowledge would be irresponsible in such situations.

This is not to say that the pastoral counsellor can have no
part to play in attending to people who are seriously ill in this
way. But he or she needs more information about the
background of such illnesses, and needs to work alongside a
doctor with psychiatric training.

Psychology and Psychotherapy—A Substitute Religion?

Many Christians take an extremely sceptical attitude
towards everything to do with psychology and psychotherapy.
I am myself well aware of the criticisms levelled at modern
psychology. These are openly expressed by secular[6] as well

as Christian[7] experts. Although psychological research has contributed to a better understanding of people,[8] many of our contemporaries are in danger of raising psychology to the status of a substitute religion. A society that no longer wants to have absolute values makes itself increasingly dependent on 'experts' to solve its problems.

By no means everything that goes by the magical title of 'psychology' is actually helpful. A fundamental distinction has to be made between *interesting ideas* in psychotherapy, and *provable facts*.[9] Many of the assertions made by various schools of psychotherapy cannot be proven. In spite of this, psychotherapy can often be helpful and effective in minor disorders, not as a result of the theory on which it is based, but because the therapist treats his clients with warmth and genuine interest, and because the patient is prepared to change.[10]

It is thus possible for Christians, as well as others, to gain help from therapy, if the therapist knows his limitations, and respects the nature (and beliefs) of the counsellee. In spite of my critical questioning, I would want to clearly underline this fact. For many people, the psychotherapist is a (paid) friend in need, with whom they can discuss their difficulties; an expert, who can show them a new way to cope with life. Unfortunately, most psychotherapists can only be of limited help in dealing with the severe illnesses which are the subject matter of this book. Their ways of thinking, however fascinating they may appear, only touch the edges of medical psychiatry in the strict sense.

Psychology, Psychotherapy or Psychiatry?

In my experience, many people find it hard to understand the distinctions between psychology, psychotherapy and psychiatry. So before I tackle the problems raised so far, I need to explain the meaning of these terms. Figure 1:1 illustrates these different areas in a diagrammatic way.

PSYCHOLOGY describes the human 'psyche' in general terms, whether it is healthy or sick. It concerns itself with an individual person's experience, thought and behaviour. The term 'psyche' was used in the Bible long ago. In the New Testament alone it is used no less than 101 times and is translated into English as 'soul', 'heart' and 'life'.[11] The word 'logeia' also occurs in the Bible and means 'compilation', gathered knowledge', 'teaching'.[12] Psychology thus means 'gathered knowledge or teaching about the soul'.[13] In connection with Psychology during the last 100 years the most diverse models have been developed to describe the human being. None of these ideas can claim to have completely and correctly understood the nature of the human individual. All of them contain partial truths and point to glimpses of what we can observe in everyday life.

A psychologist normally completes a four to eight year course of studies in a University. Unfortunately, the title is not protected, so that in the last analysis anyone can pass themselves off as a psychologist.

PSYCHOTHERAPY is a general and comprehensive term for all techniques of treatment which are intended to lead to the alleviation or healing of disturbances of the 'psyche', Nowadays there are more than 200 schools, from Analysis to the Primal scream . . . a veritable 'psycho-boom'! The training of psychotherapists is very varied. Many complete a foundational course in psychology and then undergo training in one of several methods. However, there are others (particularly those who are humanistically orientated) who complete a course and then use the title 'psychotherapist'.

PSYCHIATRY, finally, is a branch of medical science. It has to do with the diagnosis, treatment, and prevention of mental illness, and other disorders of the 'psyche'.[14] Modern psychiatry is increasingly making discoveries about biochemical processes in the brain, and has made great steps forward in the last three decades concerning the treatment of severe mental illness. A psychiatrist completes a full study of medicine like every other doctor. This is followed finally by at least four or five years of training in the psychiatric and neurological departments of a hospital, with for most

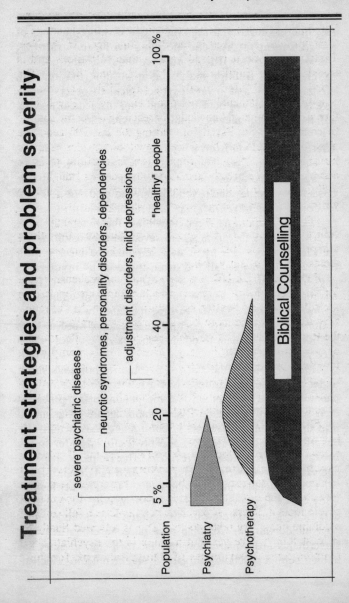

Treatment strategies and problem severity

psychiatrists a parallel training in one or more methods of psychotherapy. As can be seen from the training, the psychiatrist with his comprehensive medical and psychological training makes his main contribution with mental disease and severe psychological disorders, while psychotherapists, without the foundation of medical training still have a part to play in helping those with minor disorders.

Criticism of Psychiatry

Unfortunately, psychiatry does not have a good reputation. I can understand people posing critical questions about it. The crisis in psychology and psychotherapy has also cast a shadow of doubt over *psychiatry* as a medical discipline. *The psychiatric hospital* has been drawn into the general crossfire of criticism, as the place where severe mental disorders are gathered together. Plenty of suitable points for attack present themselves, because all too often those of us involved in psychiatry are unable to provide complete healing. Disappointed hopes easily turn into vehement complaints against psychiatry. On top of this, it is not always possible, within the limitations of doctors' professional need to keep confidences, to explain to other people exactly why a patient needs hospitalisation.

Other people on the staff of psychiatric hospitals suffer under the same difficulties. Not a few try to transfer their personal ideals of freedom and the pursuit of happiness to their severely ill patients. Disappointments are programmed into this scenario. Wolfgang Schmidbauer has beautifully described the difficulties of the professional carer in his books: *DIE HILFLOSEN HELFER* 'The Helpless Helper'[15] and *HELFEN ALS BERUF: DIE WARE NÄCHSTELIEBE* 'The Professional Carer: the marketing of neighbourly love'.[16] They make it easier to understand many of the negative experiences encountered in psychiatry and psychotherapy (and incidentally in Christian pastoral counselling as well.) Nevertheless, psychiatric hospitals and their staff must try not to hide behind psychological jargon, and be open to criticism.

Only in this way can they learn to care for their patients better.

Diagnosis: Merely Labelling?

The doubts people have about psychiatry are most strongly expressed in relation to the questions of diagnosis. A young doctor remarked recently: 'If ten psychiatrists see the same patient they will come up with ten different diagnoses.' It is certainly true that over a period of time several different names can be given to the same set of symptoms. The diagnosis of 'depression' can be applied to everything from a mild mood change resulting from a disappointment, to a severe depressive psychosis.

This makes accurate definition of symptoms all the more necessary. *We need diagnosis, in order to give appropriate treatment.* This diagnosis needs to be a consensus which helps us to evaluate the nature and level of severity of an illness, and from which we can draw inferences about its likely course.

In the case of milder depressions sympathetic counselling is all that is called for. But with more severe depressions medication is needed which in turn will vary according to the nature of the underlying illness.

So diagnosis is not just a question of putting labels on symptoms. It has to do with planning appropriate therapy. If the patient is to be helped, rather than merely suffering from the stigma of a diagnosis, the doctor must be concerned to :

- Use the clearest and most cautious principles possible in making a diagnosis.[17]
- Share any diagnosis with sympathy and consideration.
- Arouse more understanding of mental illness among the general public by open and comprehensive information.
- Offer hope in the midst of a mental breakdown,

which will pave the way for a new beginning.

Should Psychiatric Hospitals be Closed?

Do we need psychiatric hospitals any more? Isn't it time we did away with the existing structures and looked for new ways of caring for the mentally ill? These questions are posed by both psychiatrists and concerned Christians, albeit from different motives.

The call for clinics to be closed down arose particularly in the 70's in left wing psychiatric circles in Italy. The circumstances in the institutions there at that time were hair–raising in fact, and bore no comparison to the situation in many other countries. That is why the anti–psychiatry lobby wanted to bring them to a radical end.

The whole system was purely an instrument of oppression against those whom society considered abnormal, and it needed to be overhauled. 'Schizophrenia should be lived out like a simple cold', asserted Dr Basaglia,[18] a leading anti–psychiatrist of the time.

And so an enormous experiment took place. Many psychiatric hospitals in Italy were closed by law, and the patients sent home. The results were devastating. Most of the patients were overwhelmed by the sudden freedom. They no longer had anyone to care for them. Without treatment the tormenting delusions came back. Many became vagrants and beggars on Italy's streets. Others became such a burden on their relatives that over–taxed parents were driven to suicide. Soon it was clear that the law was mistaken.[19] The fatal disintegration of personality in long–term patients was irreversible. Many patients suffered greater distress during the period of freedom than they had done in hospital. Today in Italy they are trying to find new ways of caring for severely ill psychiatric patients.[20]

Humanitarian treatment of people with severe psychiatric illness requires that there should be places where they can find refuge, undergo medical assessment and therapy, and in many cases also be cared for over a long period of time. For all its deficiencies the hospital psychiatric unit is the place where properly trained personal can fulfil these conditions.[21]

Repression of Morals and Religion?

Many Christians who have had a bad experiences with psychiatric hospitals approach them with a frame of mind which is different again. They criticise the moral and religious framework of the hospital and its staff. I have often been asked: 'How can the hospital help a person if it doesn't take his belief in God into consideration or if it allows behaviour (particularly of a sexual nature) which will cause him to undergo further severe stress at a later point in time?'

Like all institutions, psychiatric hospitals are not perfect, influenced by the behaviour of individual members of staff and restricted by all manner of pressures from circumstances. The value of a hospital should not be measured by the few particular cases where the patient experiences a lack of respect and care. It is certainly true that many people working in the field of psychiatry have no personal relationship with God, and meet expressions of religion without understanding, or at best with tolerance.[22] Nevertheless, it should be remembered that many patients are admitted with disorders so severe that they can hardly be tackled as questions of faith. They are helped by simply being accepted with their troubles and receiving the appropriate medical treatment.

For many people, admission to a psychiatric hospital constitutes an enormous barrier. Nevertheless they are often really surprised by the loving attention they receive there, and the considerable benefit they gain from their stay.

During my career in different hospitals in Switzerland I have come to know many doctors, nurses and social workers who have shown great interest in the patients they have worked with, and great empathy towards them without violating their Christian convictions. We mustn't tar them with the same brush as more irresponsible therapists.

However, many pastoral workers are so disillusioned by individual experiences that they will take even severely ill patients out of hospitals in order to receive help elsewhere. Sadly, this often works to the disadvantage of the patient and his family. He will often be subjected to painful and unproductive efforts to help which only make the suffering worse, and may even drive him to suicide. In the end the only possibility remaining is to re-admit him to hospital. That constitutes the main danger of irresponsible handling on the part of Christian pastoral counsellors. Their efforts will only be understood with difficulty by the hospital, and will lead to renewed prejudice against believing patients and carers.

Psychiatry and Pastoral Care: Conflicting or Complementary?

In view of all this, does the possibility of working together exist? Can we hope for a fruitful integration of modern psychiatry and Christian pastoral counselling? In order to arrive at a conclusion on this issue, I need to briefly define what I mean by 'pastoral counselling'. Pastoral counselling helps people to cope successfully with life on the basis of biblical principles. It establishes the position of mankind from the viewpoint of the Bible and moves towards everyday problems from this perspective. The Bible makes use of various ideas which give definition to pastoral counselling. Of particular note is the word 'paraklesis' or the verb 'parakaleo'. In English this means encouragement, exhortation and comfort. Every Christian needs this, whether mentally stable or emotionally weak. The mentally stable Christian needs exhortation and encouragement to change his or her life. The emotionally weak needs encouragement and comfort in the midst of suffering.

The psychiatrist who is caring for believing people would be well advised to look for support from a pastoral counsellor. Doctors, pastors and Christian counsellors need to become increasingly aware that they are all confronted by the same human difficulties and problems. Criticism of psychiatry is not enough. Alternatives must be looked for which are biblically orientated as well as academically sound.

It only needs both sides to enter into dialogue for prejudices on both sides to be broken down, and greater insight to be gained into contemporary problems and issues in both psychiatry and pastoral counselling. With this in mind I will attempt, in the following chapters, to produce a short summary of the prevalent understanding of human nature among people involved in psychotherapy, and of the miracle of the human brain, which provides the basis of biological psychiatry.

CHAPTER 2

THE IMAGE OF HUMAN NATURE IN PSYCHOTHERAPY

You probably know the oriental fable about the blind men who were asked to describe an elephant. Puzzled, they stood around the colossus. Their eyes gazed into emptiness, but they could touch the elephant with their hands. Each one tried to describe what he felt.

The first said 'an elephant is like a spear!' 'No!' exclaimed another. 'An elephant is like a snake!' 'How can you make such a comparison?' said a third man . . . 'an elephant is like a tree'. And so the argument went on. The fourth compared the elephant to a fan which wafted cool air towards him, the fifth detected a wall and the last one talked about a rope. How could they describe the same animal in such different ways? Quite simply, one had felt the sharp tusks, the next the flexible trunk. One had embraced a leg, the other felt an ear. Finally, the fifth had leaned against its stomach and the sixth had held its tail in his hands.

The common factor in their observations was that each had restricted his description to only one part of the body. The descriptions of human nature found in psychotherapy are often very similar.

Models of the Psyche.

Most researchers and therapists describe what they have observed and established in their work with the people who come to them for advice, and even more than the blind men in the fable, they are forced to describe the complicated appearance of human nature with the help of pictures and models. The image they choose depends on the perspective from which they are viewing human nature. All too often, (whether through short–sightedness or fascination with a detail they have just noticed) they do not manage to stand far enough back for the picture of human nature they depict to be fully comprehensive.

I would like to outline four models which are instrumental in forming the predominant way that psychotherapists think about psychiatric problems. Medical scientific psychiatry builds additionally on an organic–biochemical view of human nature which I will describe in Chapter 3. Here are the four models in summary:[1]

1.   The analytical–dynamic model.
2.   The behavioural/moralistic model.
3.   The humanistic, relationship orientated model.
4.   The mystic/occult model.

It is impossible to list all the methods of each model and describe its teaching in the finest detail. This presentation can thus only be in note form (and of necessity incomplete). A good overview with plenty of reference notes can be found in the following books:

- Roger F. Hurding: Roots and Shoots. A guide to Counselling and Psychotherapy. (Hodder & Stoughton, London 1986)
- Stanton L. Jones & Richard E. Butman: Modern Psychotherapies. A Comprehensive Christian Appraisal. (Intervarsity Press, Downers Grove, ILL, 1991).

I will look briefly at the *root causes of problems* proposed from each model, and then deal with the *recommended solutions*. In the process readers may be surprised to discover that Christian pastoral counsellors have borrowed from each of the models, often without realising it.

1. The Analytical–Dynamic Model

By far the most well known form of psychotherapy today is psychoanalysis, or depth psychology. This was initiated at the turn of the century by Sigmund Freud. The Viennese neurologist started from the view that a person's reactions and behaviour patterns can all be explained in relation to early experiences and suppressed conflicts. The goal of the treatment is to bring these suppressed areas to consciousness.

Psychoanalysis in its original form requires up to four counselling sessions a week over a period of several years. Few people can afford that any longer. It is also no longer the rule that you have to lie on a couch for treatment by a psycoanalyst! Since Sigmund Freud, psychoanalysis has been further developed to a considerable degree through various schools. Although these all make use of the terms 'dynamic' or 'depth psychology', and emphasise personal development and people's (often unconscious) motives, they are nevertheless quite distinct in their procedures and the assertions they make.

Treatment through analysis is for the most part appropriate in the case of milder psychiatric disorders, because it demands something from the patient. In particular, the patient needs to be motivated enough to lay out his or her life story in long conversations to gain insight into the way things hang together, and to change. Psychodynamic therapy can be understood as a maturing process helping the patient regain his capabilities of working, loving and social interacting.

Analytical thinking has inspired many popular books. A particularly successful author is Alice Miller, whose best seller bears the title *The Drama of the Gifted Child and the Search for True Self.*[2] In this book, she endeavours to show how much parents hinder a person in his or her personal development. She sees discipline as patronising and manipulation, through which a child is prevented from expressing and living out his own needs. This leads to a deep anxiety, which must however be suppressed, so as not to lose the love of the parent. The aim of her therapy is to relive the hurts of childhood in the protected atmosphere of analytic therapy. As a result the patient will hopefully understand his own reactions, and no longer be helplessly abandoned to life as he was once to his parents.

Inner Healing

As with all psychotherapies, depth psychology depends on the therapists who practice it. Not all of them paint quite such a negative picture of parents as Alice Miller. I personally know many fine people who have an analytical orientation. They have two strengths which are especially important to me. They show empathy and take the patient seriously in his distress. And they have patience. Because they are aware that change needs time, they don't push for instant successes. Nevertheless, I have questions. Let's stop for a moment and look at what is being said in analytical therapy. It comes through in the short 'connecting words: *because* someone had painful experiences in childhood, and because they suppressed feelings, *therefore* they suffer from, for example anxiety or depression. *If* they become aware of these experiences *then* they will lose their difficulties. Similar assertions are increasingly found in Christian pastoral counselling. The catch words are 'Inner Healing', 'Healing of the Memories', or 'Emotional Healing'. Many of these books are very helpful and point to the fact that a person needs to cast off their childhood hurts with God's help. In contrast to pure analytical therapy, Christian faith offers the *possibility of forgiveness*, which goes much further than just making people aware of painful and suppressed memories. This approach really can bring a great deal of healing. Nevertheless it is tragic when, for instance, a pastor suffering from terminal cancer is told that he can't be healed from his complaint because he hasn't yet released all the hurts of his life to God.[3]

I am thinking here especially of David Watson's experience in 'Fear No Evil'.

2. The Behavioural/Moralistic Model

In the fifties many psychotherapists became unhappy with analysis. For years they had tried to uncover the hidden complexities of their patients without seeing any change. B. F. Skinner was one of the first who introduced a radical change of direction. The preoccupation with childhood was meaningless. Wrong behaviour was *learned* and *therefore* could be *removed by training*. In the course of years techniques of behavioural therapy were developed which pointed out practical ways to avoid anxiety[4] and depression.[5] The main goal was to change thinking and behaviour in a particular situation.

In the field of pastoral counselling people had also noticed that thinking and behaviour were important if the client is to break free from problems and overcome them. The approach of Jay Adams[6] is by far the best known, though one should be aware of its limitations. The exclusive emphasis on the obedience of faith and accountability may be helpful and healing for the 'average sinner'. And here it is Biblical. But it not only creates excessive demands on the Christian with severe mental illness, it also presents him with a moralising model of counselling which creates new problems for him. Nevertheless, the rediscovery of the importance of behaviour and thought in pastoral counselling is very important. The Bible says nothing about constant rummaging about in the past to understand human problems. It begins from the position that we are sinful and weak people who need God's help every day to overcome difficulties. Again and again the Christian is instructed to *lay aside* his old behaviour ('the works of the flesh') and to *put on* 'the new humanity'[7] Special importance is given in holy scripture to the *thoughts*.[8] It is our thoughts which determine our behaviour, and in part our feelings as well. The christian has to learn to be controlled by what is 'above'[9] and to be permeated by God's word.[10]

So there is room for a *cognitive behavioural therapy with a Christian basis*.[11] In what way will this be different from secular approaches like those which have been popularised by Albert Ellis[12] or Arnold Lazarus?[13] In behavioural therapy the individual's efforts stand at the centre. 'Self help', 'self control', 'personal security', 'personal liberation' and 'self healing' are the catch phrases.

Christian pastoral counselling makes an appeal to accountability and personal effort. Faith without works is dead. But it points people outwards towards God and his standard for life. God's will should be the supporting pillar of inward change, not one's own abilities and interests.

3. The Humanistic Relationship Orientated Model

For many people, behavioural therapy is too intellectual and one sided. What is the use of the best training, and simply changing your thinking, when no attention is given to feelings? This is where the third great movement in psychotherapy comes into play . . . the humanistic school.

As the name suggests, humanistic psychotherapy puts the person at the centre. The needs of the client are the measure for the therapy.[14] This approach became well known through the former theologian Carl Rogers.[15] The basic problem of every person lies in the area of broken relationships . . . with themselves and others. All the client needs from the therapist is unconditional and sensitive concern. The client must feel that he or she is accepted with their whole personality. There is no need to gain insight into deep causes. Wrong patterns of behaviour are not being questioned. The therapist is to be supportive and 'non-directive' without giving advice. Sin has no place in this concept. In every person 'the power of good' is dormant, and this will enable them to reach self-realisation.[16] In the consultation the therapist tries to create as comfortable an atmosphere as possible. The counsellor tries to put into new words what the client has first expressed in a tentative way. Emotions stay at the centre. They give direction to the consultation. If feelings can be experienced consciously, blockages are removed and the counsellee can gain entrance to his inner healing potential.

Once he has first experienced a warm relationship with his counsellor he can also build warm, fulfiling relationships with other people. In doing so, he should allow himself to be led entirely by his feelings, without looking back to restrictive moral codes imposed by either society or his faith. Humanistic group therapies also build on this philosophy. Here people find the security that they have missed elsewhere, the acceptance which is denied to them in the cold world outside. The group becomes a yard stick for their interactions and experiences. The group is their escape when life in the real world becomes too hard. In the group they find love when a marriage has broken apart.

Self Actualisation, A Mirage

Ever since the 60's, the glistening promises of humanist psychology have drawn in and moulded millions of people. They have shaken off the chains of personal accountability and allowed themselves to be guided by their feelings. In the quest for self-actualisation, they have burned their bridges to family, friends and marriage partners, only to spin themselves more and more into the cocoon of their own self.

The Zurich psychiatrist, Professor Jörg Willi, complains: 'The narcissistic rage is not satisfied even by the family in its needs for attention, tenderness, understanding and self-affirmation. It allows people to destroy the family in order to withdraw more and more into itself'.[17] Much is said nowadays about the destruction of the environment, but a much worse tragedy is the destruction of relationships through the ideology of unrestrained self-fulfilment.' Mankind is threatened today, not only by the destruction of his natural environment, but also by the destruction of his most elementary social structures'.[18]

While responsible psychologists[19] and critical theologians[20] have long since bemoaned the mess of shattered fragments left behind by humanistic thinking, this emphasis has eaten its way deep into ecclesiastical pastoral care. Even in many evangelical circles, the gospel of following Jesus has been twisted into the message of self-fulfilment.[21]

Challenge to Pastoral Care

But do we have to discard the tendencies of humanist psychology quite so thoroughly? Is group therapy not more helpful than earlier forms of fellowship? Many people have found themselves really accepted for the first time as part of a group . . . much more than they had done with their pastoral counsellor or in their home Bible study. Are we right to ignore the human longing for security and development? Does the Bible not also speak about love, acceptance and personal growth? In my opinion, it is sometimes valid to make more of a distinction between the ideological content of a therapy, and the manner in which any particular therapist approaches a client. I personally know Christians who have trained themselves in counselling therapy without taking on board the whole ideology of self-actualisation. I also know of many non-Christian therapists who have been a great deal of help to believers by their loving acceptance. I am thankful for their valuable work in attending to difficult and suffering people.

For all the doubts about its ideological basis, humanistic psychology gives an impetus to pastoral care in several ways. Love should always be an important aspect of counselling. Therein lies a challenge to the Christian pastor and to the churches. Anxiety in the face of behaviour that is hard to understand, along with an unbalanced search for sins or occult bondages, can often lead the counsellor to forget the most basic of biblical rules: listen first, then speak. The client must sense security, acceptance and compassion, because this enables him to open himself to whatever correction may be needed in his life. However, Christian belief is a totality. Love and personal fulfilment do not stand in isolation. God's love for mankind should deepen mankind's love for God. True love finds its expression, not in an egotistical living out of one's own feelings, but in accountability to one's neighbour.[22]

The very fact that God wants to satisfy our deepest yearning for love enables us to set our own wishes on one side. He can give a fulfilled life, even though we may have to live within our psychological and physical limitations.

4. *Transpersonal Psychology—Mysticism and Magic as Therapy*

The psychology of self-actualisation has taken a further step in its development. Its founding fathers—Rogers, Maslow, Pearls, to name but a few—became increasingly aware that humanity's ultimate longings could not be satisfied solely from earthly sources. They uncovered a new need of the human soul, which took them on to another goal: *the need for spiritual experience.* The way they opened up would have been inconceivable twenty years earlier, yet currently, in the wake of the 'New Age' movement, their teaching has become a 'Fourth Power' in psychology, alongside psychoanalysis, behavioural therapy and humanistic psychology.

'Magicians are among us again . . . the world of magic has been rediscovered', writes Dr Lutz Müller in the distinguished journal PSYCHOLOGIE HEUTE (Psychology Today). 'Magic and mysticism, mythology and fairy tale, meditation and imagination, dream and fantasy, eastern and western religion, shamanism, Indian culture and rituals, Parapsychology and occultism have in the last twenty years become the business not only of cranky outsiders and drop outs, but to an increasing extent also of scientists.[23]

More and more people are disappointed by long-winded monologues in the presence of their analyst, the tender words of the humanistic counsellor, and the behavioural therapists' list of goals. They are longing for an ultimate meaning to life, for sources of energy beyond the limits of their own existence. Yet they are not looking for it in Christian belief. The new magic phrase is 'transpersonal psychology'.[24] This is supposed to be the bridge between natural science and religion. The method is scientific, but the goal is religious. The psychologist has to become a priest again: 'a guide who leads his clients on to experience higher dimensions'.[25]

Their goal is the transpersonal experience which fuses humanity, nature and the cosmos into a totality'.[26] It should lead to 'new understandings of our cosmic origin'. More and more people hope in this way to gain more self confidence, and mastery over their existential fears. They see here the dawning of a new generation: not just a 'New Age' for the world, but an awakening from torpidity for their own personality. Energetic massage of the body and soul has to provide them with cosmic power.

Hypnosis and meditation lead to enhanced consciousness and new 'spiritual' experiences. With pendulum, and tarot cards, horoscope and crystal ball they try to get guidance for their life. Spiritualist mediums facilitate their contact with the spirit world, and experiences in 'reincarnation therapy'[27] help them to new understanding of their immediate conflicts.

For many Christians it will be difficult to find anything positive in transpersonal psychology. None of the four models is so clearly recognisable as a substitute religion. At best one can approve the fact that the movement has brought a spiritual dimension to psychotherapy and made the religious dimension in its widest sense a talking point in psychology. The content and the methods of transpersonal psychology are, however, diametrically opposed to Christian expressions of faith.[28]

One could almost think that there would be no parallel in Christian terms to this model, so extreme is the separation of this content from Christian belief. And yet many pastoral counsellors stand in danger of tracing back psychological problems and crises of life too rapidly to 'Negative energies', 'powerful demons', 'occult bondages' or simply 'spiritual blockages', even though this vocabulary has no biblical basis. Theories of pastoral care like this are often nearer to occult mysticism than the testimony of the Bible

Many will reply that we should nevertheless take into account the spiritual aspects of psychiatric illness in our understanding. Since these questions are given great importance, particularly in the evangelical world, but also in catholic circles, I will try to tackle them in the context of a biblical and comprehensive overview, as I describe individual patterns of illness.

Hold on to what is Good

We have now looked at four ways of viewing psychotherapy and its relationship to illness. Clearly, it is not possible to summarise and evaluate the life's work of many therapists in a few pages. However, I hope I have given a few pointers towards a better understanding of psycho-therapeutic thought. In the process it has been an important concern to point out that:

- Every model gives expression to important truths and that;
- An approach to psychotherapy is strongly dependant on the personal attitude of the therapist.

At the same time, however, it is clear that, if set free from biblical first principals, psychotherapists are in danger of forming a substitute religion. As early as 1946 the well known theologian Edward Thurneysen wrote 'pastoral care needs psychology as an auxiliary science which serves the investigation of people's inner nature and which can mediate this knowledge. In the process it has to critically set boundaries to guard against the incompatible philosophical presuppositions of psychology, which run parallel with but can encroach upon those which its own understanding of mankind gleans from the Holy Scriptures.'[29] That's why it was necessary to raise critical questions from a Christian, as well as a psychiatric point of view. These questions may perhaps provide the impetus for a re-assessment of the assertions of psychotherapy and in turn help the reader to gain a comprehensive understanding of human nature. The Bible exhorts us to 'test all things, and hold on to that which is good.'[30] In the same spirit Lawrence Crabb, for example, in his book, *Effective Biblical Counselling*[31] has presented a synopsis of biblical principles and their corresponding psychological concepts.

Careful observation of human beings can provide important keys to their behaviour, and the causes of their disturbances. The Christian's duty, however, consists in testing the conclusions of psychology against the Bible, to filter out what is useful and to arrange this into a comprehensive overview of the faith. The noted philosopher Karl Jaspers once said 'Psychotherapy needs a religious basis, but does not provide it from itself'.[32] That's why it is important for the integrity of the therapist, that first of all he can take an open and approving stance towards true faith, and secondly that he resists what experience teaches to be an almost unavoidable tendency to allow psychotherapy to develop into an ideology.

In the next chapter I would like to set out a fifth way of thinking which is indispensable to an understanding of modern psychiatry. It is not built on depth psychology and philosophical reflection, but on medical and scientific research. It will lead us into the wonderful realism of God's creation and into new discoveries about the role of the brain in the understanding of psychiatric illness. Science so far knows only a little about the process of the unique labyrinth of the brain, but even the present information opens a new understanding of disorders which those who care for the psychiatrically ill have encountered, but which, until now, have been unexplainable.

CHAPTER 3

THE MIRACLE OF THE HUMAN BRAIN

*T*he human brain is the greatest wonder of creation. This little organ weighs only 1500 grams, but contains more nerve cells than there are people on the earth, more than 10,000 million - a simply unimaginable number. Each nerve cell is joined to others by hundreds of little offshoots, and the exchange of information between them is brisker than the telephone exchange of a busy capital city. The number of *'telephone connections'* in one brain exceeds the number of stars in a galaxy. It would be more than 1,000,000,000,000! No computer or telephone exchange is in a position to store and exchange so much information in such a small space as that occupied by the human brain.

What do you know about your brain ?

Most people talk casually about their *'little grey cells'* without ever taking account of what goes on inside them. While you are reading these words, your brain is carrying out a vast number of highly complex functions. You are turning the pages with the most delicate movement of your muscles. The muscles in your eyes are adjusting so that you can see with equally sharp clarity in changing light conditions. Your retina is picking out the letters on the paper and reducing them to tiny points which the optic nerve sends on in the form of an impulse code to the visual centre, where the words are re-assembled into a new picture.

Of course the purely visual recognition of the words isn't

enough. The meaning of the words is fed in at the speech centre, so that the sentence can be compared with information already to hand. This reservoir is gigantic. It holds tens of thousands of words with every possible nuance of meaning. And there is more: Many words and sentences evoke feelings in us—both positive and negative. Often pictures which have impressed us come to the surface. So a colossal amount of information is bound up with every word, which is recalled to consciousness in fractions of a second, each time it occurs. So the description of an apparently commonplace task performed by our brain leads into the miracle of information handling, memory consciousness and beyond into the riddle the brain always poses us.   Even the well-known brain researcher and Nobel-prize winner John Eccles recognises:

'We are always on the brink of understanding the mystery that we are'[1]

For already, the little that is known is more than enough to fill whole libraries.

The Brain and Psychiatry

Knowledge about the processes inside the brain has opened up new ways to understand and treat psychiatric illness. Biological psychiatry has experienced an enormous increase in popularity since the introduction of psychopharmacy thirty years ago, and the successes seem to give it justification. Drugs have changed psychiatry. In Switzerland it has been possible to remove about 25% of the beds in psychiatric hospitals in the last twenty years alone.[2] In 1931, 155,000 people were treated in psychiatric hospitals in the German Federal Republic, for on average 300 days each. In 1983, only 85,000 for an average of 125 days, which represents a reduction of more than 70% in the number of hospital days'.[3] Many patients who would earlier have needed to be permanently hospitalised, can now live at home, thanks to medication. If we want to be given a better understanding of severe psychiatric illness, we have to apply ourselves to the miracle of the brain—a sheer impossibility in a book which aims at the same time to be understood by the average reader. For this reason I will often need to simplify things and use pictorial images to help you better understand.[4]

Modern knowledge about the brain has made the division between *'organic'* and *'psychiatric'* illness more fluid. Earlier only brain damage and degeneration of the brain through ageing were recognised as *'organic'* disturbances, especially in literature concerned with pastoral counselling, though also in psychoanalytical circles.

This view can be compared with an investigation of a defective telephone exchange in which the engineers pay attention only to the broken switches and corroded cables, whereas we know that the effectiveness of a telephone exchange depends on connections being properly made. These cannot be corrected simply by repairing the existing components. In the same way, we have now become aware that the important thing about the brain is not just the number of *'grey cells'*, but how they exchange information with one another.

A map of the brain

Where are the movements of the arms and legs steered from? Where is the memory situated? Which part of the brain processes the sounds of a thundering organ prelude, and which the colours of a summer meadow? Which area directs our speech? And which centre tells us we are experiencing hunger, thirst, or tiredness?

The answers to these questions stem from a mass of tragic experiences. They have been gained as a result of observing people who have suffered from brain damage in an accident, or as a result of a tumour. In them it became apparent, for instance, which functions were affected if someone was injured on the left temple. In this way, over the years, it was possible to build up a map of the brain. Figures 3-1 and 3-2 give a rough overview, of which the descriptions in text books are much more detailed. Nevertheless, even the most comprehensive presentations are something like a map of the world on which one looks in vain for the streets of a particular city.

Figure 3-1

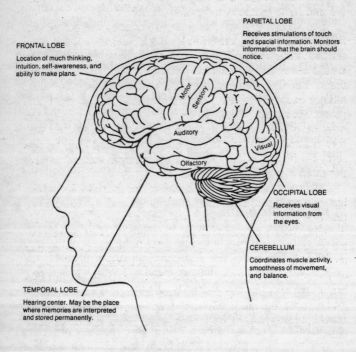

PARIETAL LOBE
Receives stimulations of touch and spacial information. Monitors information that the brain should notice.

FRONTAL LOBE
Location of much thinking, intuition, self-awareness, and ability to make plans.

Motor
Sensory
Auditory
Visual
Olfactory

OCCIPITAL LOBE
Receives visual information from the eyes.

CEREBELLUM
Coordinates muscle activity, smoothness of movement, and balance.

TEMPORAL LOBE
Hearing center. May be the place where memories are interpreted and stored permanently.

An external view of the human brain.

The Search for Personality

When Trevor* re-joined the youth group, after his severe motor-cycle accident, everyone rejoiced with him. *'What? were you really unconscious for four weeks? No-one would know to look at you now'* said his friends. Again and again he had to point to the scar on his forehead, but otherwise, there was nothing wrong with him. Yes, he could move everything, and he was as athletic as before, yet something was different. No-one could quite say to begin with what it was.

The young man who seemed so venturesome before was now quieter and less cheerful. He did his work well, but often walked off in the middle of it to eat a snack. If rebuked, he would react in an excessively injured way, and burst into tears. Yet five minutes later, he would embrace his boss, talking exuberantly. He behaved the same way in the youth group. Previously, faith had been very important to him, but now he often seemed indifferent. Towards girls, he was forward and obtrusive. If someone reprimanded him, he was sorry for his behaviour, but after a short time seemed to have forgotten everything once more.

Trevor has sustained an injury to the frontal lobe, which has connections to every part of the brain, and co-ordinates its functions. It seems a centre is situated here which controls thought, behaviour and feelings. The discovery of this fact at the beginning of the thirties gave many scientists the hope that they had at last found the location of the personality, indeed of the soul. Attempts were made to change people through brain surgery, but the results soon proved disappointing.[5] Today, such operations are only carried out in rare cases of severe aggression or epilepsy, when other methods have failed.

---

*Names and circumstances are altered in all examples

Figure 3-2

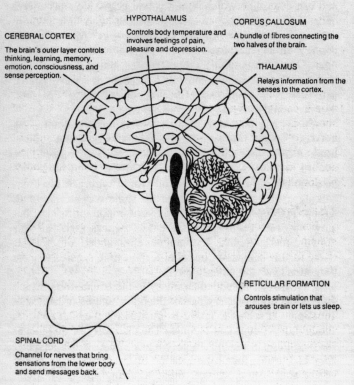

An inside view of the human brain.

The World of Brain Cells

Since then the world of science has turned its attention to research what goes on inside the actual brain cells. Each cell is a world on its own, as complex as a computer. In a multitude of tiny organs highly specialised biochemical substances are produced, which are of the highest importance for the correct functioning of the brain. They can store data, and can determine which impulses will be passed on to other cells. Every cell is bound to its neighbouring cells through a delicate branching network of hundreds of extensions. These convey either arousing impulses or quietening, restrictive ones. One could simplify the picture by talking about brakes and accelerators, but you must imagine a car which is provided with hundreds of brakes and accelerators. You would need a computer to work out when and how the car should move. However, this is what is happening in each nerve cell many times a second. When the arousing stimuli predominate, the cell begins to fire a staccato of impulses across its nerve fibres. When the restricting signals predominate, it becomes calmer.

The Miracle of the Synapse

Earlier, people imagined the brain as a great electrical system. With the help of graphs of brain electrical activity (E.E.G.) it was possible to identify the *'jamming stations'* in the brain of an epileptic person, which led to the uncontrollable muscular spasms of a fit. It could also be demonstrated that an impulse was conducted as a weak current along the nerve fibre. But how could the signal be communicated to the next cell? Research with the electronic microscope revealed the existence of bud-like thickenings at the end of each nerve fibre, which were separated from the membrane of other cells by a minute gap. This bud became known as the *'synapse'*. This small invisible thickening is so wonderfully made that the synapse soon took the centre stage in brain research. Figure 3-3 shows a diagrammatic representation of a synapse.

Biochemical substances are stored permanently in the little vesicles. When a nerve impulse arrives these vesicles empty into the synaptic gap. The substances that are stored within them act in a similar way to hormones. They are thus the essential carriers or messengers between the nerve cells. for this reason they are called neuro-transmitters. These

Figure 3-3

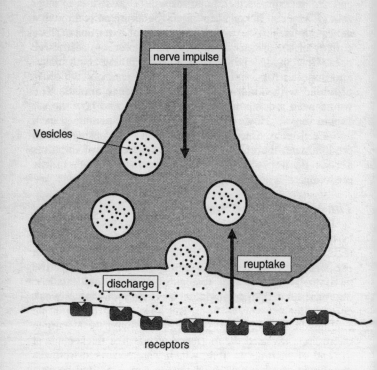

neuro-transmitters can pass on quite specialised information to the neighbouring cells. They work like a key which will only fit a certain lock, but this means that there has to be such a lock, or receiver, on the membrane of the neighbouring cell. The interplay between transmitter and receiver is regulated by a whole range of other substances (neuromodulators, enzymes). So far, science is only partially able to unravel the exact code. Nevertheless researchers have already made sensational discoveries.[6]

Valium—A Synthetic Neurotransmitter

It has been a well known fact that not everyone experiences pain in the same intensity. A friend described an interesting experience to me. He was on a mountaineering expedition, on a steep face when a storm blew up. Time was short. He banged the irons into the granite, with all his strength, in order to reach the summit as quickly as he could. When he reached the top, he noticed a strange throbbing in his thumb, and was shocked to find that it had been badly bruised, quite blue and bleeding . . . yet during his climb he had felt no pain. How was that possible?

The neurotransmitter gives us the explanation. Today we are aware of various substances in the brain which we call *'endorphins'* or *'encephalins'*, which display a distinct pain—restricting effect. Many encephalins produce a calming effect. Others can release anxiety. A research team in Basle succeeded in demonstrating that there are receptors in the brain which bind with the widely available tranquilliser Valium. From this it can be deduced that there must be substances in the brain, produced by the body, which exercise a calming action, like valium. The opposite is also possible, that valium prevents anxiety releasing substances from binding themselves to these receptors.[8]

One thing is certain: biochemical substances play an important role in our feelings, whether it be panicking anxiety, or cheerful relaxation, nervous unrest or inner calm. However, resorting too hastily to tranquillising pills may be a dangerous shortcut to inner peace. The person may become calmer, but no longer learns to grow through the adversities of life. On the other hand, one should not conceal the fact that even Christians can fall into a crisis where the nervous system is in such an uproar that the *'furioso'* of the anxiety arousing substances drowns out the *'piano'* of the calming neurotransmitters. The result: the person affected becomes nervous, tense, anxious, and cannot sleep. Even despairing cries for help in prayer do not subdue the agonising fear and bring the sleep they long for. This is where psychiatry finds justification for introducing the responsible use of tranquillisers and anti-depressants within the framework of a Christian understanding. These medications can open the way for a person to become so much more at peace that they can listen to what God says once more. Of course, in the process the person needs also to be shown how he can contribute towards his own relaxation and be made aware of the ways in which his pace of life is unhealthy.

The Autonomic Nerve System

Feelings do not only take place in the head. Fear is more than just a thought and depression involves more than just simply looking at things through dark glasses. Often body language can say more than can be expressed with words. These are age-old observations, but they have been freshly understood and scientifically researched during this century through psychosomatic studies. Our speech is rich in images which give expression to the relationships between body and soul:

- We rack our brains over a problem which gives us a sinking feeling in the pit of our stomach.
- We have a heavy heart and sorrow brings a lump to our throat.
- Someone gets cold feet and their hair stands on end.

Such figures of speech are not just flowery ways to describe feelings, they say something about the connection between the brain and the body. In the last decade, brain research has succeeded in lifting the veil to some degree from this psychosomatic area. It is, of course, a well known fact that every person possesses two nerve systems:

- the motoric system, which directs the movement of muscles, and
- the autonomic nerve system.

The autonomic nerve system weaves its way through all our internal organs, with the most delicate threads, and reaches every lymphatic organ, however small. It is supported in this by a wide variety of hormones (neuropeptides). Nowadays we are aware of dozens of message-carrying substances which control digestion alone. A small quantity of one newly discovered hormone can lead to massive suppression of the appetite and may possibly have a role to play in anorexia nervosa.[10] Others alter body temperature, breathing, or the heart beat.[11] These substances are released in the central region of the brain, where the seat of the feelings is thought to be, in the thalamus and hypothalamus, and it is now known that they are closely connected with the encephalins. So it is no wonder that psychological moods often lead to alarm signals in the autonomic nerve-system. A beating heart, difficulty in breathing, hot flushes and cold shivers, constipation, or loss of appetite. Stress puts the whole autonomic nervous system into an uproar, and this *'wailing siren'* in the organs reinforces anxiety and depression in an unfortunate psychosomatic cycle and often brings the patient for the first time to the doctor who then speaks of a vegetative psychosomatic disorder.

The Brain—a Computer?

We have now learned some of the brain's secrets: the nerve cells, the synapses, the neurotransmitters and the autonomic nervous system . But what does it need to integrate this accumulation of cells, and biochemical substances into what we know as the human brain? Basically, the interaction of millions of brain cells makes it possible for us to think feel and act. I will quickly admit that the precise details of how the brain is governed are so far hidden from us. We cannot increase our knowledge as we would like, because any interference would destroy these delicate structures. Nevertheless, we have in broad brushstrokes an idea of the important reactions in the brain which allows us to make better guesses as to how and why major disturbances can come about in the context of psychiatric illness. By way of illustration, I would like to briefly outline a model of the brain as a biological computer. In doing this, I am not wanting to reduce the human spirit to the level of a simple machine. That would be mistaken and stupid. However, the new discoveries in brain research[12] show that many of the brain's activities do resemble those of a computer, for instance:

- information gathering (through the sensory organs)
- information sorting (is that shiny thing on the floor a piece of glass or a coin?)
- storage of information (memory)
- information retrieval (e.g. knowledge in a test)
- application of information (e.g. knitting a pullover according to a pattern)

Many disturbances can be better understood with the help of this model, schizophrenia for example (see chapters 9 - 11). In the process they lose their aura of the sinister and demonic, making room for a more compassionate viewpoint through which genuine help will be possible for the first time.

The requirements of biblical pastoral counselling must not be diminished through this way of thinking about the brain. God has made our brain much more wonderful and complex than any computer will ever be. The way in which the brain processes information can be compared to a computer programme which can at times be disrupted and distorted. But which information determines the brain's thinking and behaviour will depend on a person's life history and inward attitude.

Spirit or Brain?

What then is the significance of the human brain in a Christian view of man? Has modern brain research rendered the soul an unnecessary myth? How can the discoveries of biological psychiatry be harmonised with spiritual concerns?

If the brain is the control centre of a human being, what is the significance of the soul and spirit?

Many people seem to look at a person as a purely organic being controlled by an immensely complex computer called the brain. They believe that with the progress of brain research, human behaviour and its disorders will be understood more fully and even better treated. On the other hand, the serious scientist is aware of the provisional nature of his knowledge—*'We know in part'*. This sentence from the Apostle Paul is still valid in the twentieth century. The results of brain research have revealed something of the wonderful construction and complex functioning of the brain, but hasty conclusions about the nature of the human being would be premature.[13]

For this reason I find no contradiction between the discoveries of brain research and what the Bible says about human nature. The 'spirit or the brain?' question is as complex as the existence of a symphony. What makes a symphony unique? The way the instruments are constructed, or the notes in the score? The dots of printer's ink on the paper, or the sound waves? All these are needed if we are to experience the glorious sound of a concerto. So it is with the the human spirit.[14] It needs the brain as an instrument, to communicate itself to others, but the spirit in itself is eternal, beyond material constraints. Personality is like a symphony. The question is:

Who writes the score of a person's life?
Whom does the person allow to finger the chords of his instrument?

Again, the sound of a symphony is not only dependant on the virtuoso skill of the musicians, but on the creators of the instruments. Instruments are impermanent. They can go out of tune, become warped or even broken, and they cannot always be repaired. This is where we find the limits of the symphony of our lives. Here we see the significance of our view of human nature. Damaged instruments are worthless and distressing. For materialists everything stops with the extinction of the brain function and for the society of the strong, the weak are unimportant and inconvenient. But for God, even a broken harp with hanging strings is of eternal value.

CHAPTER 4

HOW MENTAL DISORDERS DEVELOP

*H*ow do psychiatric problems really come about? Is there a common outlook, a comprehensive model on which our understanding of the development of mental illness is based? Is it possible to develop explanatory models which will help us understand people suffering from psychiatric disorders, but which remain true to the reality of life? Is there a biblical view of man which not only explains sinful behaviour, but can also be applied to severe illness?

These questions have taken up a great deal of my attention over the past years. While psychotherapeutic models certainly explain milder disorders, they often do not lend themselves to be applied to severe psychiatric conditions. On the other hand biological psychiatry often does not answer people's personal problems and questions.

In what follows, I would like to present a simple model of the development of mental illness which is both academically sound and biblically based. This is not so much a question of fundamentally new ways of looking at mental illness, but rather a didactic model which will attempt to tie together in a new way things which are already known. The reader will be already aware of much of it. Other aspects will be unfamiliar. Don't allow this to deter you from following my train of thought.

In the diagram on page 56 three important areas are

outlined which favour the development of a mental illness. In the past, one segment of the circle would often have been emphasised in a one-sided way and presented as the sole cause of all mental illness. Today we are increasingly aware that all these factors are bound together and interact mutually on one another. I have picked out two levels of understanding:

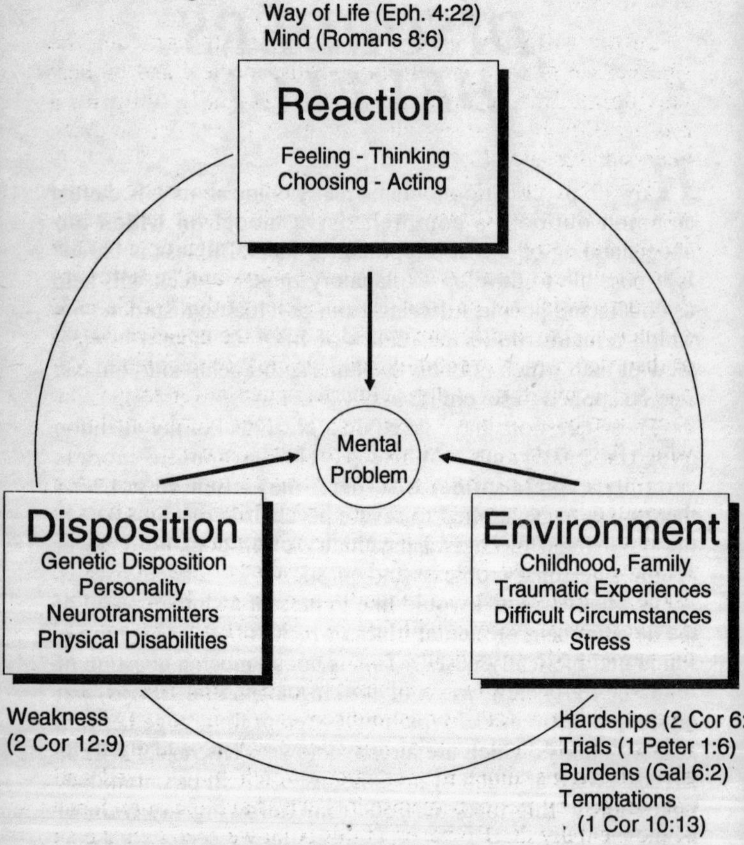

Way of Life (Eph. 4:22)
Mind (Romans 8:6)

Reaction

Feeling - Thinking
Choosing - Acting

Mental
Problem

Disposition
Genetic Disposition
Personality
Neurotransmitters
Physical Disabilities

Environment
Childhood, Family
Traumatic Experiences
Difficult Circumstances
Stress

Weakness
(2 Cor 12:9)

Hardships (2 Cor 6:
Trials (1 Peter 1:6)
Burdens (Gal 6:2)
Temptations
(1 Cor 10:13)

Figure 4-1: The Building Blocks of the Model

1. GENERAL CONCEPTS as they are commonly encountered in our culture and language, thus: 'disposition', 'environment', and 'reaction'.
2. BIBLICAL CONCEPTS which correspond to these three areas, thus: 'weakness', 'troubles', 'trials', 'burden' and 'testing', along with 'way of life' and 'mind'.

In the following pages we are going to consider the significance of each area from both the medical and biblical viewpoint. In the process we will gradually build up a mosaic-like picture which will make it easier for us to understand mental illness.

This will furnish us with a comprehensive basic model which not only explains severe illness where hereditary factors and brain chemistry are of primary significance, but also provides pointers to help us understand less severe disorders which are only on the perimeter of this book's field of interest. Obviously, the emphasis is on the negative causes of disorders which eventually need psychiatric treatment. Yet pastoral counsellors and psychiatrists must never forget that every person also has 'resources', in other words attributes which help them cope with their difficulties better.

The question posed in psychiatry and pastoral care is often expressed in a causal, therapeutic form: 'How has this person come to be so disturbed, and how can we make him better?' However, I would like to plead for a further question to be asked; a 'goal-orientated-rehabilitative' one: 'How can this person manage to cope with life in spite of his weakness and the burdens life gives him to bear?'

Even people with severe mental illnesses still have healthy areas which it is valid for us to discover and nurture, as far as is possible. In the course of this book I will repeatedly try to give directions about the resources which can be used and encouraged by pastoral counsellors who have the confidence of the mentally ill. However, at this point we need to make an inventory of the factors which lead to psychiatric disorders as their final outcome.

1   Disposition: The Stuff We are Made Of

'I can never understand why I am so weak', complains Mrs Klermann. 'Even as a child I preferred to play on my own, because I could relate best to my dolls. I had dear parents. It wasn't any fault of theirs. I was simply not as robust as my brothers and sisters. I had difficulty with gymnastics at school because my left hand was crippled from birth. During puberty I was often melancholic and couldn't get off to sleep until midnight. I had no reason for it. My mother had also been a sensitive woman. If we children got a bit out of hand she would burst into tears. Sometimes I can be as capable as other women, but if I don't get enough sleep, everything inside me starts to tremble. My stomach seizes up, and I can hardly eat anything. I often have terrible migraines since that accident with the scooter. I have tried many tonics but they've been very little use. I can just about get my work done . . . I haven't strength for anything more.'

Mrs Klermann consulted the psychiatrist during a depression following the birth of her second child. What clues can we pick up from these few sentences? What did she say which will help us to understand her depression?

Please refer again to the diagram on page 56. The area of difficulty in Mrs Klermann's case is less to do with her reaction (her thoughts and behaviour) but obviously more to do with her disposition and her situation (the birth of a child brings with it changes of circumstance which are not always easy to cope with).

If we consider for a while first the disposition of the patient, this can be separated out into four areas:

a) Hereditary factors
b) Birth trauma
c) Physical illness and autonomic nervous reactions
d) Temperament

Many physical and psychological weaknesses are inherited. Time and time again it can be observed that a patient's family members have had similar difficulties to his own. The most important mental illnesses, schizophrenia and endogenous depression, are often (though not in every case) found in the ancestors and relatives of an affected person. This can be repeatedly demonstrated in case studies of twins and adopted children.[1] And there is more: in the case of certain brain conditions, for example Alzheimers disease, it has been possible to locate the exact place in the genetic code which led to the fatal degeneration of the brain.[2]

Mrs Klermann made two statements about her ancestors. Her delicate mother had a tendency to depression (this came to light in the course of an interview with her). An uncle had to undergo psychiatric treatment several times because of depression. These statements gave a clue to the fact that a tendency to depression was already present in her genetic inheritance.

However the functioning of the brain is not only affected by hereditary factors. Birth traumas often lead to physical and mental disabilities as well. Being deprived of oxygen can be especially serious, and can lead to brain damage in the baby who suffers it. This will result in learning difficulties and behavioural abnormalities which may last into adulthood, even when they receive frequent and exceptionally good treatment.

Mrs Klermann did not suffer severe trauma at birth. She is quite intelligent, but nevertheless she continually experienced hindrance from her lame hand when she was doing gymnastics and many practical tasks. With her depressive nature she withdrew (reaction) and increasingly became an outsider.

Then came the scooter accident when she was sixteen. She suffered a concussion of the brain, followed by searing headaches and bed-rest for two weeks. Since then Mrs Klermann has been sensitive to weather changes. She often has to sit down and can't cope with her work. Migraine brings the whole body into uproar. She feels sick, she perspires, her heart pounds and she burns with hot flushes. These symptoms are caused by the autonomic nervous system which weaves all the internal organs together like a fine net. Emotional upsets often set off alarm signals in the autonomic nervous system, which then goes out of its normal rhythm. Many people are sensitive as a result of hereditary factors and often suffer as a result of their physical problems which are then labelled as 'nervous breakdown' by the doctor.

Temperament—Inherited or Acquired?

Since ancient times researchers have been concerned to understand and classify human behaviour better. The most famous system originated with the Greek physician Hippocrates, the 'father of medicine'. Through his keen observation he created the teaching about the four temperaments: sanguine, choleric, melancholic and phlegmatic. Since then, of course, we have come to realise that human character can be described by using many different words.[3]

Every personality has its own strengths and weaknesses. No type comes in a 'pure' form. One person will often combine qualities from many sources into one unique whole. And above all, no type is worse than another.

Where does personality come from? Is it inborn, or formed through our upbringing? Is it the result of our natural disposition, or of what we experience in our environment?

The question of intelligence has in particular been a subject of keen investigation.[4] So far, psychologists have not been able to reach a common mind. Many indications favour the idea that intelligence is a gift, which can however be developed by upbringing, although it cannot be increased (or reduced) at will.

Things are somewhat different when it comes to personality traits. Many observations indicate that the basic pattern of our personality is laid down from birth. Spirited, outgoing children will also be extrovert at a later stage. Quiet, withdrawn children will equally tend towards introversion at a later stage. Children often show a similar temperament to their parents or grandparents. However the data to hand indicates that our disposition—more clearly than is the case with intelligence—is formed by our environment.[5] A child is still enormously capable of development. Fearful boys can grow up to become brave men. Well behaved, placid girls can later suffer from nervousness and anxiety. The basis for these developments has yet to be fully explained.

Let's come back to the example of Mrs Klermann with which we began. She already showed a tendency to introversion as a child. She preferred to be alone and could play with her dolls for hours while her brothers and sisters were running about outside with other children. In spite of a loving home and the foundation of a good I.Q., she developed a sensitive personality with a tendency towards depression, the foundations of which were already to be discerned in her disposition.

My Strength is Made Perfect in Weakness

Is there a term used in the Bible which equates to what modern psychology and psychiatry would label as 'pre-disposition'? Yes and no.

Certainly, the authors of the books in the Bible would not have recognised the terms we use today. There is no talk of genetics, of the brain or of 'temperament'. But they nevertheless continually describe people who, through no fault of their own, were weak and disabled, whether as the result of birth or later experiences. In the Bible we meet people with various personality traits, from impetuous Peter to doubting Thomas. We read of Timothy's digestive problems, and of the raging pain that brought Paul to the edge of doubt.

The Christians in the New Testament churches were not all 'heroes of faith'. Many struggled not only against their sinful nature, but against their inability to equal the achievements of the 'strong' in the church. That's why Paul exhorts the Christians in Thessalonica 'to encourage the faint hearted, to help the weak, and to be patient with everyone'.[6] And he knew what he was talking about. He understood weakness from his own life experience. Three times he had pleaded with God to take away his terrible pain, the 'buffeting of Satan's messenger', but his prayer was not granted. But God promised him His support in spite of his weak physical disposition. 'Let My grace be enough for you, for My strength is perfected in weakness.' Paul goes on: 'for this reason I will boast above all about my weakness, so that the power of Christ may dwell in me   That is why I am happy in weakness . . . for when I am weak, then I am strong.'[7]

2.   Environment: Life's Burden

The second life-forming factor which contributes to our understanding of psychiatric disorders is environment. Everyone passes through burdensome experiences, whether it be abuse in childhood and youth or disappointments and illness in later life. On top of this, 'fate' deals unforeseen blows, and trying situations come about which affect the course of your life. Often a person will be given a burden which he will have to carry for the whole of his life. All these burdens are nowadays summed up under the label of 'stress'.

A person's life history will often give the psychiatrist or pastoral counsellor a better understanding of the mental troubles experienced by a client. I would like to classify these burdens under the following headings:-

a) Family background
b) Childhood experience
c) External limitations, for e.g. the 'burdens' a person has to carry
d) Trying circumstances
e) Unforeseen events
f) Surrounding tense relationships

Childhood Influence

A child's personality is formed for the most part in the family. This is where the foundations are laid. So much depends on the experiences it has in the first three to six years . . . whether it experiences security and love, care and warmth . . . whether it learns with the passage of time to set aside its own needs and take thought for others . . . whether, on the other hand, it undergoes strife, violence and even sexual abuse . . . whether it knows what rules govern the process of living together . . . whether it is spoiled and 'molly coddled'.

But is it really true that the future is decided by those childhood experiences? Many depth psychologists would answer 'yes', but recent studies contradict this thesis.[8] In an outstanding book the Stuttgart psychologist Hansjorg Hemminger poses the provocative question: 'Is childhood destiny?'[9] He shows by many examples that childhood experiences alone do not determine the course of a person's life.

He writes: 'A child from a problem family begins its independence with a smaller capital of good experiences, helpful ways of thinking and appropriate emotional responses than others . . . research over a long period showed us children who overcame a hard destiny and matured through it. It showed us others who broke down after a sheltered childhood as a result of their refusal to become independent. There were those people who made good use of the capital of their good childhood, and others who were unable to resolve the conflicts in which they had been locked since their troubled childhood.'[10]

In a penetrating way, he pleads for people to live in the present: 'only present behaviour, present decisions and present thoughts have reality. Each nostalgic look backwards to a beloved or hated past, and every forward look towards a hoped or feared future becomes an illusion, if the present is blotted out and lost sight of.'[11]

Living With Stress

Even so, the present can be difficult enough, so difficult as to make a person feel they just can't go on any more. Again and again in the course of my work I meet men and women who have been brought to the end of their resources by external experiences and have developed mental problems ranging from depression to psychosis. I remember the preacher who had to stand by helpless while a girl drowned at a youth camp in Sardinia. I think of the mother whose child lay in the children's hospital for almost a year. The daily visits sapped her energy. The constant uncertainty robbed her of sleep and in the end led to a temporary psychosis which made a stay in hospital necessary.

STRESS is one of the most important factors contributing to the development of illness in our time. Stress can lead to the development of severe psychiatric crises in people who have a hereditary weakness and little opportunity to overcome their problems. In modern psychiatry people talk about 'vulnerability', by which is understood the degree of sensitivity a person has to react under pressure with either psychiatric disturbances (e.g. depression) or physical symptoms (e.g. heartburn) or behavioural changes (e.g. withdrawal, fits of anger). The relationship between stress and vulnerability, or to use biblical language, between testing and weakness, can be represented by a curve.

From figure 4.2. it can be easily seen that under increased stress a person comes nearer and nearer to the edge of mental dysfunction. How soon they reach this point depends on their hereditary sensitivity. A person with strong nerves (line (1)) can hold out if he suffers a car accident, he is criticised at work, or if he loses his dog. He will not develop any psychiatric problems. But if someone suffers a higher sensitivity (line 2) they will find that even relatively insignificant problems will lead to disturbances of sleep, anxiety and psycho-somatic difficulties. However, this diagram should not be interpreted too literally. Each person not only has their own level of sensitivity, but their own internal resources to cope with stress.

Figure 4-2

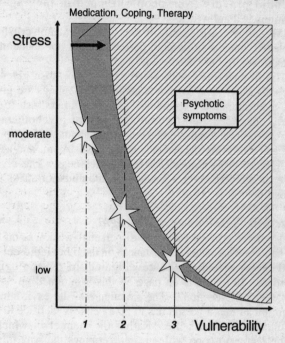

Stress and Vulnerability

Mentally healthy people can learn to meet stressful situations with a new attitude and to grow through them. Yet in my medical career I have come to know many people who, despite all their best efforts, simply could not succeed in countering stressful situations with just a prayer or a change of their inward attitude. They had to learn rather to avoid unnecessary stress and so prevent themselves wandering too near the danger zone of mental distress.

Patient in Tribulation

The Bible knows about the stresses people can undergo. It talks about tribulation[12] and burdens,[13] about opposition[14] and testing.[15] The Psalms present us with some of the most splendid prayers from people trapped in inescapable situations.[16] Paul writes:

'We are hard-pressed on every side, but not crushed, perplexed, but not in despair, persecuted, but not abandoned, struck down, but not destroyed.'[17]

The descriptions in these passages echo those given in psychotherapy. The trouble is named, and feelings are given free, even dramatic, expression. However, in contrast to the purely one-sided, self-centred approach of psychotherapy, Biblical pastoral counselling does not set about stirring up the mud and analysing the wounds of the past. Again and again the light of hope shines into the helplessness. The divine 'nevertheless' becomes a foothold in the midst of stress and opposition.

Reaction: The Power of Thought

A person's inward attitude to personal weakness on the one hand and adverse circumstances on the other represent the third factor affecting the development of psychological disorders. In the table on page 56 this is summed up under the keyword 'Reaction'. The situation and the environment do not mean that a person has to be a helpless sacrifice to the circumstances of his life. Rather the manner in which a person learns to cope with stress determines the way things develop. To a large extent their thought, will and behaviour help to determine what effect an experience has on their psyche.

A person's reaction to an experience is determined by what they think about it, how they evaluate it. This simple concept has been around in psychiatry for a long time:

An Experience (A) gives rise to a feeling (C) For instance, someone may become depressive (C) because he has been criticised by his boss (A).

Figure ABC

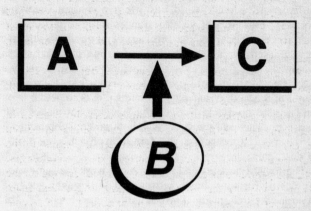

But between A and C stands an important connection, the way the person evaluates (B) an experience, the significance they assign to it. One person will say at the end of the day: 'The boss had a bad day today, never mind, things will be better tomorrow.' Another will blame himself and be afraid of losing his job. Both had the same experience, but evaluated it quite differently.

Our 'Belief System'

There is nothing new about the idea that the way we see things affects our psychological reaction to them. Way back in antiquity the stoic philosopher Epictetus wrote 'people are not disturbed by experiences but by their perception of those experiences.'

So, what forms our view of experiences? Each person develops ideas during the course of his life, a system of beliefs about how he can become happy and cope with life.[18] Everyone longs for love and recognition and strives to find some way of satisfying this longing. Yet on the road to fulfilment lie many hindrances. Again and again people have to learn to live with unfulfilled wishes and come to terms with the reality of a harsh world. So life is a continual learning process. Early negative experiences have a particularly formative effect, as do later experiences which are accompanied by intense feelings or strong physical stress symptoms. To give an example, imagine you are bitten by a dog. The terrible feeling of menace and fear, as you are caught in the teeth of an angry growling dog is something you don't forget too quickly. Even the thought of it makes your heart beat faster and the sweat stand out on your forehead. It will be a long time before you dare to approach even a little lap-dog again.

Feelings of hostility and rejection can work the same way. The result for your basic attitude: 'I will never get in a situation like that again. I will not allow it to happen'. The result for behaviour: you avoid every encounter which carries with it the risk of a fresh rejection. In this way the rejection changes not only your inner life, but also your contact with your environment—a vicious circle develops, a whirlpool which can eventually draw you into serious psychiatric problems.

A New Way of Thinking

The earlier the foundations for a mature way of life are laid, the better a person is able to cope with living. I am personally convinced that the wisdom of the Bible gives us the best foundation for a fulfilled life. The Bible uses two key words which equate with the psychological concepts of 'cognition' (thought) and behaviour. It continually speaks about the importance of 'mind'[19] and 'way of life'.[20] King Solomon once said in Proverbs 'Be careful how you think; your life is shaped by your thoughts.'[21]

So a Christian will be at pains to allow his world of ideas to be shaped by the testimony of the Bible. That means more than just positive thinking. God's word requires us to put off the old nature, to 'walk in the Spirit';[22] grow in love[23] and put on the new man.[24] That can only happen if we open ourselves clearly to God's working and allow all our thinking and behaviour to be shaped by His word.[25]

But is it that easy to change our thinking? Even people who are self-aware cannot simply forget rejection, snuff out the memory of tragic experiences and replace them with a 'hallelujah!'. The healing of memories takes time.

And for many people—I am thinking here of my schizophrenic and severely depressed patients—the biochemistry of the brain is sometimes so severely disturbed that they are no longer able to control their thoughts.

This situation is not foreign to the Bible. David knew times when the thought of God no longer comforted him, but rather cast him down,[26] and Paul knew of the presence of God even in times when he could no longer pray.[27] Herein lies hope for believing Christians who go through the severe mental breakdowns which I will describe in the following chapters.

PART 2

PROFILES OF MENTAL ILLNESS

CHAPTER FIVE

NEUROTIC DISORDERS - AN OVERVIEW

Mr Morton takes things quite seriously. Everything has to be in order. His day is rigidly timetabled, without a free moment. He knows how many minutes it takes him to get from home to work, and he has counted the number of traffic lights which might hold him up on the way. There are exactly 39 divided among five intersections. Mr Morton is a librarian, and in his profession, a conscientious workforce is vitally important.

However, not everyone is completely happy about his work. His wife, for instance. She often suffers as a result of his excessive demands. By the time he comes home, the children are already in bed. He can't come home earlier, because he has to tidy up the library. 'All he's doing is standing books on end again!' says his wife, bitterly. 'He can't abide books leaning at an angle. But he never thinks about me and the children'. Even his boss has expressed concern, because in his craze for orderliness he neglects more important duties in the library. He has threatened to cut his wages.

Mr Morton is finally visiting the psychiatrist, under pressure from his wife. Has Mr Morton just got a kink, or is he neurotic? Is he eccentric, or is he a sick man? Is his behaviour merely peculiar, or is it sinful? Can he change, and should he . . . and if so, how?

Are We All Neurotic?

Small anxieties, compulsions and depressions are part of everyday life. Nearly everyone has 'illogical' fears and inhibitions in certain situations. Do you know that uncomfortable feeling of fear when you cross a bridge? You know perfectly well it will bear your weight and the balustrade will prevent you falling off, but even so, you are glad when you reach the other side. Fear can also influence relationships between people.

How often do we hold back from doing something because we are afraid of being rejected, or of failing. We all know the strange feeling of butterflies in the stomach before an exam . . . in other words, in a situation where we are not completely in control. In these situations fear leads to psychosomatic reactions, even among healthy people.

Other people discover compulsions within themselves. A tune refuses to go out of your head. You try to read every car registration number, or you adjust your steps to fit the pattern of the pavement slabs. Other people have difficulty in leaving a room unless it is cleaned and tidied up. And what housewife has not checked and double-checked that she has turned off the oven?

Normally we can suppress these fears and compulsions. We can stop the thoughts, divert our attention, think about something else and forget the disturbing impulses. Added to this, the fear on the bridge never becomes as strong as in a person with an anxiety neurosis who will make a gigantic diversion to avoid the bridge. The housewife only checks the oven once or twice. She doesn't fall into the hour-long rituals of the obsessive compulsive person. During a difficult meeting you may experience a rise in your pulse rate, but it is nothing like the physical collapse which takes place in a psychosomatically over-sensitive neurotic. You can put up with critical remarks without turning them over and over in your mind like a neurotic depressive person.

The frequently stated opinion that everyone is fundamentally a little neurotic constitutes an unjustified extension of the concept of mental illness. Professor R. Tolle makes a striking observation in his textbook: 'Not every conflict situation which is difficult to resolve and is accompanied for a while by mood changes and autonomic nervous reactions, is to be labelled as a neurosis. The more unique a person is, the more complicated and susceptible to disruption his life will be. We do not need to talk about a pathological disturbance. So long as the prescribed neurotic reactions and symptoms cannot be established, it is better to speak of a 'crisis situation'.[1]

Psychological Reactions in a Crisis

The psychologically healthy person is in a position to control his thoughts, enjoy life, cultivate relationships and fulfil the duties with which life presents him. He can order and direct his thoughts and feelings in such a way that they contribute to his achieving a conscious adjustment to the circumstances of his life.

In a crisis, things change. Tense relationships or excessive demands at work, severe illness, or the sudden death of someone you love can lead to mental exhaustion. Then more and more energy is needed to deal with the burdensome circumstances and thoughts. This energy is then unavailable for coping with everyday life. You become sensitive, physically and mentally. The autonomic nervous system goes into uproar and presents the whole spectrum of psychosomatic reactions from heartburn and racing pulse to trembling hands. Sleep is often disturbed, and this leads in turn to further exhaustion.

In this weakened physical state, depressions, fears, compulsions, hysterical reactions and aggressive outbursts can surface, which you would not otherwise have recognised in yourself. Somehow you don't quite have yourself under control any longer. Impulses suddenly find expression, which in good days you were able to keep shut up in the 'junk room' of your mind.

A middle-aged man undergoes considerable suffering

when his wife seeks a divorce from him. His zest for life is extinguished. Sometimes he wakes during the night bathed in perspiration after a nightmare. Long forgotten experiences from his childhood come to the surface of his memory. At the office, he continually has the feeling people are talking about him behind his back. He feels inadequate, and avoids his colleagues.

A young mother is plagued during her quiet time by the horrible thought that she might do something to harm her baby. 'I would never do it, but the thought just won't leave me alone. It is like a compulsion', she complains.

It seems that every person has certain weak points in their make-up, typical patterns of experience and behaviour, which only break out under pressure. That explains why, in the examples above, one person reacted in a resigned, depressive manner, while the other reacted to difficulty in an excited, dramatic way. But crises pass, and these typical symptoms slip into the background once more as they go. The help of a doctor or medication is not needed in every case to overcome a crisis. God has created us with many ways of conquering mental crises and their disturbing 'neurotic' symptoms. Often the simple old proverb holds true: 'time will heal'.

It's a different matter for people whose whole life is controlled and overshadowed by neurotic symptoms, often without an obvious external trigger. For them good advice which is helpful in times of crisis doesn't lead to the desired improvement. The source of their suffering is themselves and their own restrictions and weaknesses. Friends and relatives don't understand them, in fact their behaviour can be a burden for their relatives and those around them. In these cases the psychiatrist talks about 'neuroses' and 'personality disorders' in the strict sense.

Exactly What is a Neurosis?

Neuroses are the most common psychiatric disorders, and

can be found in something like 10% of the population. Women are affected twice as often as men. The boundaries between slight and severe cases are fluid. Milder versions are labelled as 'personality disorders' and if these are included in the total, you arrive at a figure of something like 30% of the population suffering from 'psychogenic disorders'.[2] Under this heading a confusing diversity of human behavioural weaknesses are lumped together, ranging from relationship difficulties to sexual problems, from overwhelming anxieties to psychosomatic troubles. The existence of the 'neuroses' has been disputed in psychiatry to this day. New text books go so far as to completely delete the term from their diagnostic vocabulary and to talk about 'personality disorders' along with anxiety, obsessive - compulsive syndromes or major depression.[3] If I still speak here of 'neuroses' I do so according to the traditional understanding of the term, in connection with which I must clearly define myself so as not to misuse this diagnosis.

Severe neuroses, such as those I am about to describe in the following pages, are genuine illnesses with clearly describable symptoms and consequences which, like other similar mental illnesses, can lead to considerable disability.

As Figure 5.1 on page 78 indicates, most people who suffer from their own self and their behaviour, also have healthy aspects. With the exception of the most severe states (to the extreme right of the diagram) their situation allows them to live self-sufficient lives. So one seldom sees neuroses in hospital, chiefly because they do not run such a dramatic course as, for instance, psychoses. But the ordinary G.P. and the pastoral counsellor will meet these disorders with a proportionately greater frequency.

The course of neuroses is manifold. Basically it is a matter of long lasting disorders which can however become

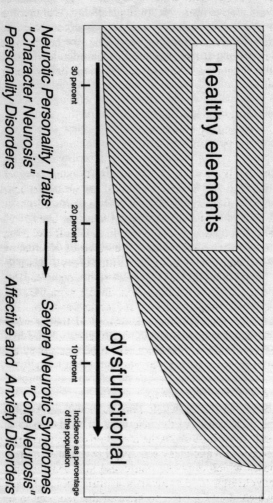

Figure 5-1

Degree of Severity of Neuroses

stronger or weaker in phases. You can often observe a basic personality disorder onto which a more severe disorder is 'grafted' from time to time. Not infrequently this will involve a change of symptoms, that is to say passing across from one symptom to another, so for instance someone who begins with anxiety symptoms can later move into a chronic depression. Research has shown the following pattern in the development of symptoms.

20%	are eventually cured
60%	eventually improve, and
20%	become more established.

The outcome in the case of the last group often involves complete invalidity, where those afflicted are no longer able to fulfil their duties and to follow their vocation in life. Neurotic disorders are most common between the ages of 20 and 40 years. Thereafter symptoms begin to tail off and those afflicted find a better equilibrium. Often a vestigial situation develops—a life within limits which still allows a bearable existence. Many neurotically ill people are of course capable of work, but most allow for limitations in the work they do. They are often lacking in energy and enthusiasm for life. They live a retracted life and lose most of their earlier interests. So a neurotic person will find a certain relief in a general withdrawal from life, which has to be paid for by the sacrifice of their earlier desires, dreams and relationships.

The Causes of the Neuroses

In the course of history whole libraries have been written about the possible causes of the neuroses. Nevertheless even today, we still know little about the conditions which give rise to these disorders. While many schools of psychotherapy rely on hypotheses which only see one cause and one therapy, modern psychiatry tends towards a multi-disciplinary approach which allows for the problem of the neuroses to be tackled with impartiality. One fails to do justice to the neuroses by representing their suffering merely as a failure to react properly at a psychological level. Neurotic disorders—like other mental illnesses—are caused and influenced by many different factors.

For a long time and until today, it has been assumed that neurotic disorders developed during early childhood. Unresolved conflicts, often with sexual colouring, led to fixation at immature levels of childhood development. More recent research has not been able to confirm these theories.[6] In my opinion false conclusions have been drawn from correct observations. Neurotic people do, in fact, manifest strange patterns of behaviour which often appear to be immature and childish.

The person with an anxiety neurosis won't dare walk along the street alone. The hysteric makes a drama out of the smallest event. Yet this does not mean we can deduce that the disorder developed from damaging experiences in childhood. Once again we need to distinguish between interesting comparisons and demonstrable causes.

Disposition - Environment - Reaction

The development of the neuroses and personality disorders involves a complicated interplay of disposition, environment and reaction (see the diagram in chapter 4, p. 56).

DISPOSITION: There is much to suggest that hereditary factors play a part even in the development of neuroses. Large scale studies of twins have shown a significant tendency for neurotic symptoms to coincide in them, particularly anxiety and stress syndromes.[7]

Another factor that can foster neurotic development is mild brain disorder (e.g. following meningitis or lack of oxygen at birth).

Those affected are less mature in the way they cope with the conflicts of life than are people with unimpaired brains. They more frequently manifest difficulties in adjusting, and inappropriate behaviour, which provoke others to a counter-reaction driving them further into isolation.

Environment

Surprisingly, neurotic people do not undergo stressful experiences to any greater degree than other people. However, it seems that the neurotic hypersensitivity leads to altered perceptions of relations and events, making average interactions stressful to the individual. Neuroses occur more frequently among people from sheltered and pampered families. Our prosperous society with its almost unending freedoms openly encourages the development of neurotic behaviour. The more possibilities open to a person, the more frequently they will fall into internal conflict. Conversely, neuroses recede into the background in times when there is an external threat (for e.g. in war time).

Reaction

Emotional wounds can cause a person so much stress that he wraps himself increasingly with a neurotic shield to protect himself from further hurtful experiences.[9] Every attempt to lay aside this 'protective shield' is accompanied by enormous feelings of anxiety. These make it difficult for the afflicted person to enter relationships with other people in a relaxed way. Only when he feels a deep trust can he dare to lift his visor a little and show another, more mature pattern of behaviour.

Neurotic people are often imprisoned within the force-field of their own neurotic conflict. On one hand they suffer as a result of it and struggle to get free. But on the other hand the inner tensions it produces do not allow them to develop alternative ways of thinking and behaving, even when these can help them to greater freedom.

Under mild levels of stress these inappropriate reactions can be identified, and worked on. But I continually find that in extremely stressful situations it is simply impossible for the patient to react any other way, however much he would like to do so.

Diagnosing Neuroses

The diagnosis of neurotic disorders is made from the person's life history, and the difficulties they describe. Many disorders, for example obsessive-compulsive disorder, are easily recognisable. In other cases it is necessary to spend a long time with the patient and if need be, to rule out other illnesses, before the nature of the illness can be determined.

A neurosis is hardly ever found in an absolutely pure form.[10] Almost always several other 'neurotic strands' are in interplay with it. So depressive people usually also suffer from anxieties and compulsions. Compulsive personalities, in spite of their suffering, are hardly depressive, but people with anxiety neurosis are often bothered about their bodily functions in a hypochondriacal way. To simplify things, you could imagine the neurotic character traits as a kaleidoscope which continually shows new patterns of light, colour and form as it is turned.

In spite of their manifold expression, there are common threads which run through and link individual disorders. The following signs of illness occur in most types of neurosis:-

- insecurity
- inhibitions
- disturbances relating to making contact
- mood changes
- reduced efficiency in performance of tasks
- accompanying physical changes related to the autonomic nervous system.

To describe the individual forms of neurotic disorders in detail would exceed the limits of this book. The interested reader will need to refer to psychiatric textbooks for further information. From conversations with pastoral counsellors and people who are suffering from neuroses, I know that those who suffer from physical problems and depression can nowadays count on a great deal of understanding. But there is much more difficulty in getting people to accept anxiety, compulsion and hysterical behaviour as illnesses which can occur even among Christians. In their less severe forms they often cause great difficulties to those who suffer from them, their relatives, and their pastoral counsellors. Those affected suffer not only from themselves, but also from lack of understanding and inappropriate attempts to heal them on the part of many fellow Christians.

For this reason, the next chapter will explain these syndromes in a brief and general way and give help for pastoral counsellors in dealing with these people.

CHAPTER SIX

ANXIETY, COMPULSION, AND HYSTERIA

We live, they say, in an age of anxiety. In spite of all his progress, modern man is full of anxieties and insecurities. They range from worries about ecology to fear of a nuclear catastrophe, from fears that are justifiable in a dangerous world, to groundless anxieties about contracting an incurable illness. Of course, fear has always been around, indeed, it is just part of human existence. Anxiety takes many forms and affects even committed Christians, yet it does not seem to be unconquerable. Although many people suffer from anxiety especially in times of personal crisis, they still manage to find ways of living with the fear and doing what they have to do. Normally they are open to receive encouragement, and comfort, and after a short time they regain their inner peace.

For a neurotic person, it is different. His thoughts, feelings and behaviour are moulded by fears of an abnormal intensity, which he is unable to put into words. Not without justification, Riemann has described the neurotic personality disorders collectively as 'basic forms of anxiety'.[1]

Anxiety as an Illness

For many people, fear becomes a sickness which rules their whole life. When this happens, the doctor will start to talk about an 'anxiety syndrome'. Often no adequate basis for the anxiety can be found. Even in the simplest of situations, the afflicted person becomes tortured by overpowering feelings of confinement and threat which at times grow to the level of absolute panic, all with—from the normal point of view—little reason. These fears give rise in the process to accompanying physical symptoms, which are as intense as if the afflicted person really was facing immediate danger.

A woman described her anxieties to me in the following memorable way: 'If I look out of the window, I'm afraid of falling out. I never get into a lift, because I'm afraid it might get stuck. I'm continually afraid of an accident when I'm in the car, and at work I'm afraid all the time that I may make a mistake and lose my job. For years I've sent my husband to do the shopping. If I go to church, I'm afraid of the crowd, my heart goes into my mouth and I can't catch my breath. If I read my Bible, I get afraid that I'm not saved, or that I'm possessed by an evil spirit, even though I really know I'm in God's hands. I simply can't fight against these fears. Things do improve when I take medication . . . but even then I'm afraid of becoming addicted.'

Imprisoned by Fear

People who are afflicted in this way often live in a panicky fear of fear. For this reason, they avoid everything that provokes fear or increases it. A gifted young man will not dare to accept a further promotion because every time he has to take on increased responsibility, he is attacked by massive anxieties and headaches. A housewife will prefer to stay in the security and peace of her home, rather than go shopping and be constantly plagued by the fear of fainting and falling down in public. Every heartbeat, every feeling of nausea increases her fears and drives her more and more into isolation.

People with anxiety syndromes suffer enormously as a result of their limitations, but they would rather live alone and withdrawn than set in motion the terrible feelings of anxiety which they remember from previous experiences.

Quite often a patient with an anxiety syndrome will find

enough resolve to gradually allow himself to face situations which would previously have caused him to be afraid. He dares, perhaps with the help of a pastoral counsellor or a therapist, to try to make the first few steps. To begin with, he is able to suppress the slight unease which rises up inside him, but then the old fears begin to surface once more. In the end he reaches a point where he is no longer able to blot out the distressful inner tension. Time after time, he gives up in resignation and draws back into the security where he still feels reasonably comfortable. Figure 6.1 represents this state of affairs in the form of a diagram.

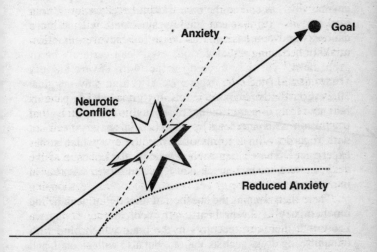

Figure 6-1
Fear as a hindrance on the path towards a goal

(The thick line shows the path to the goal (e.g. going shopping alone). After a few steps the fear level rises (broken line) and becomes stronger and stronger until the sick person decides to withdraw from his intention. The dotted line shows the fear suppressed (for e.g. through medication), making the attainment of the goal possible.)

Help With Anxiety Syndromes

Is there then any way of suppressing this anxiety far enough to allow the afflicted person at least the possibility of reaching simple goals with a tolerable level of anxiety? Could they not relax, if they really wanted to? Perhaps they could become free of their anxieties, if they worked through their childhood experiences or received 'inner healing'?

I would be really glad to answer with a simple 'yes'. But anyone who has shared the pain and futile search for healing of a person with a severe anxiety syndrome will be more cautious and compassionate. With less severe anxieties, relaxation techniques of various kinds can certainly be of great help,[2] yet they have no effect with severe anxiety syndromes. In fact, the experience of getting only marginal alleviation by their conscious effort to relax, leads patients into new fears of never finding relief at all. The same kind of frustration is experienced by people with anxiety neuroses with regard to those forms of psychotherapy which stress experience. These often achieve exactly the opposite of the desired effect, namely increase of fear, and further withdrawal into resignation.[3]

There then remains the question of directly influencing the biochemistry of the brain through medication. Today we know that there are receptors in the brain which bind with tranquillising drugs such as Valium, but also with alcohol, and lead to an obvious relaxation. Against this background it can more readily be understood why alcoholism and misuse of tranquillisers is so widespread.

It is as well to be aware of these dangers, but one should not be deceived by them into overlooking the fact that there are also illnesses in which it is possible to bring about a marked improvement with the help of sedatives. Even in the anxiety syndromes we have been describing, medication can bring enough relief to the patient to keep the fear at a bearable level. Recent studies in the development of addiction have shown on the whole that the problem has been exaggerated.[4] Many patients do not increase their dose, and use the drugs very responsibly.

This reduction of fear by medication can be achieved much more easily, if those afflicted feel themselves to be accepted by their doctor, and are encouraged by him to live within the limitations which are imposed on them by their fears. Herein lies an important role for the pastoral counsellor. The Bible describes human fear with sympathy and yet realism in a way that no other book does. Jesus does not always promise his disciples complete freedom from anxiety, but says to them: 'In the world you will have tribulation, but be of good cheer, I have overcome the world.'[5]

Obsessive-Compulsive Disorder (OCD)
A Breakdown In Thought Control

The 25 year old bank employee looked in the peak of health. Yet he had been incapable of work for the last six months. His suffering had begun several years earlier. When he was counting money, he began to be plagued with the thought that he might have made a mistake. Often he had to check several times to make sure he had counted the bank notes correctly.

He was weakened further by an attack of influenza. He didn't dare to go to work, for fear that other people would notice his problem. If he was putting a piece of paper in the typewriter he had to repeat the process ten times. If he received post addressed to him, he had to check every letter typed on the envelope. Often it would take him half an hour to open it. If he went to the toilet, his family knew it would be occupied for an hour.

The compulsion spilled over into his spiritual life. He had

to kneel to confess every little sin, straight away (with his knees in line with the pattern on the carpet and his face in his hands). He often had to repeat the prayer several times, because he wasn't sure he had done it right.

His day became full of complicated rituals and agonising mental compulsions. Only when he was asleep did he find a few hours respite. He knew well enough that his thoughts were irrational and his behaviour unnecessary, but if he tried to resist them, an uncomfortable tension and fear surged within him, which only subsided when he gave way to the impulses.

This example illustrates the suffering which can be caused by obsessive-compulsive disorder. This syndrome is fortunately rare (something like 5 in 10,000) and does not always take such a dramatic form as the case I have just described.

It is usual to distinguish between obsessive thoughts, compulsions, and compulsive behaviour. Obsessive thoughts are determined by fears (for example, that something will happen to you or someone else) or by feelings of guilt (you might do something wrong, or be responsible for someone else's misfortune). Compulsions are often ruled by the pressure to do something dangerous or improper (for e.g. sticking out your tongue) or—especially tormenting for Christians—to say something obscene or blasphemous. Of course, the sick person does not act on the impulse, but suffers enormously as a result of his sensitive conscience.

Compulsive actions, finally, manifest themselves in repeated acts, for instance to do with counting, controlling or washing.

The causes of obsessive-compulsive disorder have long been in the dark, and we still do not have all the answers. However, recent research has brought fourth exciting new evidence that there are biochemical processes in the brain involved with OCD.[6] In these patients, the brain is obviously not capable of properly processing and containing information (for instance concerning the cleanliness of the hands), thus repeating behavioural and thinking impulses outside the control of the conscious will.

How these compulsions come about has so far been only inadequately explained. Personally, I lean towards the view that these illnesses involve a complicated functional disturbance of the brain.[6] In these cases it is obviously not capable of properly holding a piece of information (for instance concerning the cleanness of the hands) in such a way that it sends out new behaviour and thought impulses regularly and without the control of the will.

Don't Enforce Release

To date there is no therapy for the obsessive-compulsive disorder syndrome. Release from compulsions cannot be forced. Throughout the decades all the great psychotherapists have advanced theories about the causes of obsessions and compulsions yet the success of the therapies has been modest. 'Compulsion', so it is said, 'is the favourite, but most difficult, child of psychoanalysis.' The same holds true for the attempts of pastoral counsellors to help with severe compulsions. Antidepressant medication, such as Anafranil or Prozac, can bring about substantial relief in about 40 per cent of the patients. Thus, even if success is only limited, treatment should be attempted in order to make the inner tension bearable.

There is hope especially for those patients who suffer from passing obsessive-compulsive symptoms, which can occur under stress in a fragile person. In these cases the distressing compulsions can abate in the course of weeks or months without any specific treatment being given.

What can the doctor and the pastoral counsellor do for the person suffering from OCD and for his or her relatives? If nothing else is achieved, it is of incalculable value for them to be just accepted with their affliction. Because of his healthy appearance, the sick person often experiences little understanding on the part of those around him. People find it hard to believe that he is unable to work. An important task for the carer is therefore to take the sick person seriously and to provide a significant occupation within the scope of his limitations.

The afflicted person will find real relief in being able to talk openly at regular intervals, even if the problem of the compulsion remains.

The Hysterical Personality

While people with neurotic fears, compulsions and depressions withdraw from others, 'hysterical' people try as far as possible to turn the attention on themselves. Doctors and pastoral counsellors encounter here, not sad and inhibited 'wallflowers' but attractive, spirited and articulate personalities, for the most part women.

They have anxiety too, but unlike the disorders described so far, people who react hysterically are afraid of 'the final, the inevitable, of the urgency and the finiteness of our craving for freedom.'.[7]

They show a pattern of excessive emotionality and attention-seeking. Even minor events are met with intense, yet superficial feelings, ranging from rapturous enthusiasm to deep disappointment and temper tantrums. Nothing bores them more than the routine of an ordered life. They are easily impressed, often responding in an overly trusting way to any strong authority figure. They tend to accept new convictions and beliefs strongly and readily, but without being firmly rooted, often changing their minds after a disappointment.

These characteristics lead to great problems in relationships with other people. Hysterical personalities make a charming impression to begin with and make friends easily. But once a relationship has been built, they become demanding, self-centred and inconsiderate. In their longing for unconditional acceptance and recognition they make themselves excessively dependent on others and take them completely under their wing. However, if the other person tries to create more space there will be reproaches and dramatic demonstrations of emotion.

Helpless fastening on to people can reach such a level that it leads to attempts to suicide. By their immature behaviour they destroy the very relationships they long for so intensely.

Sexual problems occur frequently in this context. Hysterical people often suffer from excessive expectations of themselves and their partners and tend to escape into sexual fantasies. The reality is usually quite different and disappointments are inevitable.

Often they also complain of bad health, general weakness and headaches. In times of great stress it can include experiences which resemble those which accompany psychosis. One lady complained to me during a breakdown[8] that she saw the world around her completely distorted, as if seen through warped glass. Often she felt like a spectator in the theatre of life. When she recovered, these disturbances fell back into the background.

It is not surprising that hysterical people often suffer from intense disturbances of mood, especially when external circumstances change and as a result relationships are broken. Depression can be the result.[9]

Once in a while so-called *Conversion symptoms* can occur, where, for example, afflicted people express their inner helplessness in such a way that a lameness develops in the legs which cannot be explained organically. In these situations we speak of a hysterical neurosis in the narrow sense.

Setting Boundaries

Hysterical patients are a particular challenge for the doctor and the pastoral counsellor. Frequently it is hard to tell what is genuine and what is acted out. The pastoral counsellor often has to experience for himself how the person normally behaves with other people. They are often unpredictable, even for the carer.

To begin with, one is overwhelmed with compliments: 'You are the first person who has taken me seriously and listened to me. You understand my problems and sympathise with them. You are a wonderful pastor!' But then more and more is demanded: frequent telephone calls, often at impossible times, the wish for home visits and other signs of special interest. They often present their complaints in a dramatic form during the consultation, garnished with elaborate details which always leave you wondering if there isn't some exaggeration. Yet these people are totally convinced about their experiences and react to probing questions from the pastoral counsellor with complaints and doubts about his ability to understand them.

Christians with hysterical traits will tend to explain their experiences in terms of supernatural influences. Often they introduce occult powers into their presentation, so that they can give the most colourful descriptions of demonic oppression. They then require the pastoral counsellor to deliver them from their 'possession'. In the process dramatic scenes are played out which are intended to demonstrate to those present the demonisation of the patient. If the minister tries to set limits on the fulfilment of their request, the afflicted person can react in a demonstrative way, going into a 'huff' and showing annoyance and exaggerated disappointment. Often they will then turn to a pastoral counsellor who has a 'greater anointing'.

This doesn't mean that the role of spiritual help during a hysterical crisis has to be played down. Words of scripture and prayers can lead to an impressive calming and release from inner conflicts. On the other hand the 'emptiness' of relying on the comfort and empathy of regular pastoral care often seems too tame to the afflicted person because it doesn't lead to the instantaneous change they want to see.

It is wrong to dismiss the behaviour of hysterical women as 'theatre'. Here also we are dealing with a pattern of behaviour in sensitive people, which they are not always able to control. Indeed, in hindsight, they are often appalled themselves at the way they have allowed themselves to be led astray by their feelings. With a general calming of the circumstances of stress there usually comes also a subsiding of the hysterical symptoms.

What these people need amid the tossing waves of their feelings is a rock which can provide them with security, protection, and a haven . . . a pastoral counsellor who takes them seriously, but reacts to their feelings with relaxed moderation and sets the necessary boundaries. A pastoral counsellor who still remains firm in response to their immature, angry reactions without rejecting them, and a pastoral counsellor who encourages and helps them to be self-sufficient in spite of their desire for dependence.[10]

Does Faith Make You Neurotic?

Neurotic conflicts and insecurities often lie concealed behind the questions and concerns of faith. The pastoral counsellor is affected in a particularly painful way when someone's spiritual life is controlled by anxieties, compulsions and hysterical behaviour, since these do not only affect people who are hostile to the faith. Even upright and serious Christians can suffer from neurotic symptoms which are coloured by spiritual ingredients. It is no accident then, that in literature one finds the idea of 'ecclesiogenic' (church produced) neuroses or 'toxic faith' being put forward. For example, the protestant theologian and psychotherapist Helmut Hark describes the problem of religious neuroses in a comprehensive study.[11]

He defines the idea of 'ecclesiogenic neuroses' in the following way: 'the term 'ecclesiogenic neuroses' designates those, in the many layered spectrum of mental illnesses, which take on a religious garb and are induced by excessive religiosity. Whether piety and faith act like a poison in the mind or work like a medicine to produce happiness, depends on the dose administered, and the religious education received from parents, school and church.'[12] He contradicts the widespread, if long since superseded, assertion that religion makes people ill, and backs this up statistically. By means of

a comprehensive questionnaire, he compared 139 patients
who were seeking therapy because of mental difficulties with
234 people from a 'healthy' control group. In the process he
reached the following conclusions:

'In the group of patients thus described an inverse
correlation could be discerned between psychoneurotic
problems and religious orientation. This can be statistically
demonstrated: The more pronounced the psychological
problem, the smaller the level of religious orientation and
piety. Conversely it can be demonstrated that a weighting
towards religious orientation reduces psychological
difficulties. Our research thus confirms the experience of the
individual case, that a life of faith reduces and disrupts
neuroses, while a positive piety leads to the healing of such
disorders.'[13]

Possibilities and Boundaries of Pastoral Care

What possibilities then are open for the pastoral counsellor
to help a person suffering from a neurosis, from a biblical
stand-point? Much has already been alluded to in the sections
on individual illnesses. Knowing themselves to be accepted
by the counsellor, having the opportunity to talk, and to
receive special prayer, can have an enormously helpful and
calming effect for the sick person. The pastoral counsellor
has at his or her disposal in personal conversation, and
pastoral preaching, a wealth of biblical examples which
demonstrate over and over again that it is among the weak
with their suffering and their limitations, that God chooses to
show his power. It is often important to help the enquirer
towards a new understanding of God.[14]

Yet in severe cases there will not always be a certain goal
for the pastoral counsellor. Ought he to be satisfied in these
cases with just comforting and supporting the client? Does he
need to confront him with his unconscious conflicts and
hidden motives? Should the client not at least give expression
to his pent up feelings? Or is he simply lacking a fulfilled
spiritual life?

The therapy ideas found in the literature of psychiatric and pastoral counselling are legion. Yet it is noticeable how many neurotically sick patients eventually abandon their odyssey from therapy to therapy and withdraw once more into isolation without their treatment having brought the healing they desired.[15] These failures are hard both for the pastoral counsellor and the secular therapist to cope with. Often they end up blaming either the sick person, his parents, or their own lack of ability.

But is it the case that these people are just unwilling to change, or are the therapists perhaps expecting too much? I often ask myself whether a delusion of productivity typical of our technological age is not being carried over into the pastoral care and therapy of neurotic patients, even if camouflaged by a thick covering net of Christian and psychotherapeutic jargon.

Empathetic Compassion

The empathetic compassion of the pastoral counsellor seems to me to be of particular importance in the care of a person who is suffering with a long term neurosis. He should be in a position to recognise the client's unhealthily sensitive personality behind the presenting questions concerning faith and doubt, and to respond appropriately. The following quotation from Blumhardt mirrors something of the basic attitude of the pastoral counsellor in dealing with nervously weak people.

'As as rule I don't make too many demands on the afflicted person, pressurising them to pull themselves together. For I have already seen bad results from that approach. I stick with the advice: 'Do what you can, and if you can't manage something easily, give up and keep calm. And don't be afraid, either, that everything will soon be lost. Don't worry if you feel yourself bound up against your will and in a bad mood with God and the things of God.

Furthermore, I would like to say something more to comfort you. In hard affliction, you must not immediately try to apply yourself to the Bible or some other book for your edification. If sometimes you feel that every word applies to you, I understand, but if all you find there is strangeness, you will get no blessing, read what you will. So it is when your inclination is set against prayer. What good does it do to force yourself? Then I often say 'leave it!' If you really have to pray like that because people tell you you must pray on your own, well, you can very easily do it in such a way that the irritation hardly finds a way to hinder it. Think how you have the whole Bible already contained in the simple 'Our Father'. There you will find reference to the Name, the Kingdom and the Will of God, the generous care of God in giving us food, the forgiveness of sins, and as you also forgive, prayer against temptation.'[16]

Notice with what obvious sympathy Blumhardt takes up the pressures of the 'afflicted' without lapsing into spiritualisation or psychological jargon. He takes up what the client says at the level of his problems of faith and relieves his burden by pointing him to simple basic Biblical truths.

This keeps the pastoral counsellor from condemning and rejecting the sufferer as a 'miserable sinner' and 'doubting Thomas', even if the desired healing is not achieved for the time being. It helps the counsellor develop the ability to steer the client through his weaknesses with patience and love.

CHAPTER SEVEN

DEPRESSION - AN OVERVIEW

'*I* don't know what's wrong with me. I haven't had any energy for the last two months at least. Nothing gives me any pleasure nowadays.' The once confident businessman spoke in a low monotone voice, his eyes downcast. 'I wake up as early as four o'clock in the morning . . . filled with an agonising fear about the day to come. I'm no use for anything any more. I'm a complete failure. I can hardly summon up the courage to telephone a customer . . . no-one's giving me any orders nowadays.'

He took a deep breath. 'But the worst thing is, God's deserted me. I used to get so much out of reading the Bible, but now it doesn't speak to me any longer. Every time I try to pray I feel condemned. I'm full of unbelief. God can't carry on listening to a person like me. I can't see any way out. Is there any help for me?'

A Despairing Search for Help

To begin with Mr. Brown tried to struggle with his problem on his own. He swallowed vitamins and went out to jog every morning. But the pressure grew. His wife didn't know how to encourage him when he complained about his difficulties. He picked up a book about conquering depression from someone in his home Bible study group. He tried to pray more, recognised his self-pity, and thanked God even for his difficulties, but the dark clouds didn't disperse. Even a prayer for deliverance from a trusted pastoral counsellor failed to bring the peace he longed for.

Mr. Brown was so aware of the sins in his life that he didn't expect to gain any help from the doctor. So he only told him that he was having pains around his heart, and said nothing about how he felt inside. The E.C.G. was normal, and the doctor didn't pursue the problem any further.

After a few conversations with him, the lay pastor of his church realised that he was dealing here with a severe depression, and referred him to me. Happy ending? No way! It took months of consultations and treatment with drugs. The road to healing was peppered with pot-holes. Days of hope were cancelled out by renewed darkness. But, in the end, the dark clouds did weigh less heavily on his mind. Time and time again Mr. Brown opened what he once referred to as 'windows of joy'. Today he is fully back in business again, and what is more important to him, he can read God's word with pleasure once more and take an active part in the life of his church. His odyssey from one therapy appointment to the next is typical of many who suffer from depression.

Christians with depression often seem to find it difficult to understand their condition and take the measures that are needed to deal with it. They suffer because even the faith in God which used to shape and motivate their life is unable to stop them walking into the valley of the shadow. They want to make sense of their trouble in the light of the Bible, but this isn't always easy for them. They do not fit the cliché of the victorious Christian. How can anyone understand someone not living in continuous joy, peace and hope, when these things are promised in the Bible? And how can anyone help a person who is suffering, not just from a passing mood, but from a severe depression?

Most Christian books deal with circumstances which in psychiatry would be labelled as slight to moderate depressions. The advice they contain is helpful, effective, and even biblical, in overcoming temporary oppression. But with two exceptions, I have found little help in them for Christians who suffer from severe endogenous depressions.[1] My goal in the following two chapters is thus to show:

- the criteria by which a severe depression can be recognised;
- the connections which exist between biochemistry, environment, experiences of life, and behaviour;
- the course usually taken by a severe depression;
- the effect of a depression on a person's spiritual life;
- how to give pastoral help to someone with severe depression, and
- how to work together with the G.P. and the psychiatrist.

How to Recognise a Depression

Depression has many faces. A dark veil with a complicated woven pattern darkens the view. So before we talk about the forms, causes and treatments of depression, we first of all need to recognise the different 'woven patterns' which eventually allow us to diagnose depression.

The analysis of a typical attack of depression will be given in table 7-1. Notice in particular the duration: to justify the diagnosis of a typical (severe) depression at least four symptoms must be present for a period of at least two weeks. Milder depressions on the other hand last a shorter time and show fewer distinct symptoms. For instance, we would not talk about a severe depression if someone was in low spirits for a few days (but remained capable of work) and slept badly as a result of his worries. Nevertheless one should treat this complaint seriously since a mild disturbance of mood can develop into a severe depression in the course of time.

The accompanying physical symptoms are summarised in table 7-2. Both tables show how closely soul and body, 'psyche' and 'soma', are interwoven. The autonomic nervous system follows the swing of each upheaval of the soul.

Breathing, pulse and digestion change their rhythm and each in their way give expression to the soul's distress.

Table 7-1

Criteria for the Diagnosis of a Severe Depression [2]

A. Loss of interest and pleasure in all or almost all activities or amusements. Frame of mind: depressive, sad, dejected, cast down, irritable. Rapid changes of mood are nevertheless not typical of a depression.

B. At least four of the following symptoms must be present almost every day for at least two weeks:

1. Poor appetite or considerable weight loss (without a diet) or increase of appetite with weight gain.

2. Loss of sleep or increase in sleep.

3. Inward or outward restlessness or lethargy.

4. Loss of interest or pleasure in all usual activities, or lessening of sexual drive.

5. Loss of energy, exhaustion.

6. Feeling of worthlessness, self-rejection or excessive and unjustifiable sense of guilt.

7. Complains of reduced ability to think, concentrate, and make decisions.

8. Recurring thoughts of death, death wish, thoughts of suicide or attempts at suicide.

9. The possibility of another illness must be considered if non-depressive irrational ideas and bizarre behaviour occur or if the depression is connected with a previous psychosis.

Table 7-2

Physical Symptoms Accompanying Depression (Not Always Present)

- Headaches, dizziness, dryness of mouth
- Feeling of pressure or tightness in the neck or chest
- Outbreaks of perspiration, pounding heart, palpitations, disturbances in the rhythm of the heart, pain in the region of the heart.
- Frequency of micturition, pain in the lower part of the body, disturbances in sexual function.
- General loss of energy and absence of freshness.

Leading questions can quickly provide clear contours to the disorder. Here are some suggested key questions[3] which the pastoral counsellor or the doctor should ask:

- Are you still able to enjoy yourself?
- What's the situation where your interests are concerned? Is it any different to what it was before?
- Are you less able to take initiatives than you were several weeks or several months ago?
- Do you feel alert, or exhausted during the daytime?
- Do you feel nervous, tense or anxious inside?
- Do you find it difficult to make decisions?
- Have you been experiencing disturbances of sleep?
- Do you experience any pain? Do you notice a pressure on your chest?
- Do you notice any loss of appetite? Have you lost weight?
- Do you have any difficulties of a sexual nature?
- Have you had a tendency to be more thoughtful recently?
- Are you plagued by the thought that your life has become useless?

Christians will complain in addition that they have 'lost their joy in the Lord', that the Bible doesn't speak to them any more and that they have difficulty with prayer. They will no longer be certain of their salvation and will feel, because of their sense of guilt, that God has rejected them. As well as being afraid of other people and the demands of everyday life, they will be afraid of a God who, in the distorted view of a depressive person, is angry and vengeful. Depression often signifies separation. Everything which previously gave purpose to life disintegrates and no longer gives support. Often even a person's faith goes through a deep crisis. The dark veil of depression lies not only over everyday life, but also over the experience of God's presence.

All of these afflictions can occur in varying degrees of severity, in diverse gradations of grey tones, like the boards of a weathered wooden house. A valuable tool for measuring the severity of the depression is provided by the Beck Depression Indicator (BDI).[4] If a client registers less than 11 points, they are not described as depressed. 12–19 points indicates a slight depression, 20–26 points represents a moderate depression, and more than 26 points shows a severe depression, provided that the symptoms also last more than two weeks.

Table 7-3

The Beck Depression Indicator

This questionnaire consists of sets of statements grouped together. Read each set through carefully. Then choose the one statement in each set which best describes how you have felt this week, including today! Circle the number of the statement you have picked. If more than one statement in a set seems equally appropriate you can mark more than one number.

In each case read all the statements in each set before making a choice.

A. 0   I do not feel sad
   1   I feel sad
   2   I am sad all the time and I can't snap out of it
   3   I am so sad or unhappy that I can't stand it

B. 0   I am not particularly discouraged about the future
   1   I feel discouraged about the future
   2   I feel I have nothing to look forward to
   3   I feel that the future is hopeless and that things cannot improve

C. 0   I do not feel a failure
   1   I feel I have failed more than the average person
   2   As I look back on my life, all I can see is a lot of failures
   3   I feel I am a complete failure as a person

D. 0   I get as much satisfaction out of things as I used to
   1   I don't enjoy things the way I used to
   2   I don't get real satisfaction out of anything anymore
   3   I am dissatisfied or bored with everything

E. 0   I don't feel particularly guilty
   1   I feel guilty a good part of the time
   2   I feel quite guilty most of the time
   3   I feel guilty all of the time

F. 0   I don't feel I am being punished

1   I feel I may be punished
2   I expect to be punished
3   I feel I am being punished

G. 0   I don't feel disappointed in myself
     1   I am disappointed with myself
     2   I am disgusted with myself
     3   I hate myself

H. 0   I don't feel I am any worse than anyone else
     1   I am critical of myself for my weaknesses or mistakes
     2   I blame myself all the time for my faults
     3   I blame myself for everything bad that happens

I. 0   I don't have any thoughts of killing myself
     1   I have thoughts of killing myself, but I would not carry them out
     2   I would like to kill myself
     3   I would kill myself if I had the chance

J. 0   I don't cry any more than usual
     1   I cry more now than I used to
     2   I cry all the time now
     3   I used to be able to cry, but now I can't cry even though I want to

K. 0   I am more irritated now than I ever am
     1   I get annoyed or irritated more easily than I used to
     2   I feel irritated all the time now

3   I don't get irritated at all by the things that used to irritate me

L 0   I have not lost interest in other people
     1   I am less interested in other people than I used to be
     2   I have lost most of my interest in other people
     3   I have lost all of my interest in other people

M 0   I make decisions about as well as I ever could
     1   I put off making decisions more than I used to
     2   I have greater difficulty in making decisions than before
     3   I can't make decisions at all anymore

N. 0   I don't feel I look any worse than I used to
     1   I am worried that I am looking old or unattractive
     2   I have the feeling that changes have taken place in my appearance which make me unattractive
     3   I believe that I look ugly

O. 0   I can work about as well as before
     1   It takes an extra effort to get started at doing something
     2   I have to push myself very hard to do anything
     3   I can't do any work at all

P. 0   I can sleep as well as usual
     1   I don't sleep as well as I used to
     2   I wake up 1–2 hours earlier than usual and

find it hard to get back to sleep

3   I wake up several hours earlier than I used to and cannot get back to sleep

Q. 0   I don't get more tired than usual

1   I get tired more easily than I used to

2   I get tired from doing almost anything

3   I am too tired to do anything

R. 0   My appetite is no worse than usual

1   My appetite is not as good as it used to be

2   My appetite is much worse now

3   I have no appetite at all anymore

S. 0   I haven't lost much weight, if any lately

1   I have lost more than 5 pounds

2   I have lost more than 10 pounds

3   I have lost more than 15 pounds

T. 0   I am no more worried about my health than usual

1   I am worried about physical problems such as aches and pains; or upset stomach; or constipation

2   I am very worried about physical problems and it's hard to think of much else

3   I am so worried about physical problems, that I cannot think about anything else

U 0   I have not noticed any recent change in my interest in sex

1   I am less interested in sex than I used to be

2   I am much less interested in sex now
3   I have lost interest in sex completely

Evaluation

Add up the total of the numbers before each sentence you have marked. The highest possible score is 63 points.

Average scores
a) No depression   11 points
b) Slight depression   12-19 points
c) Moderate depression   20-26 points
d) Severe depression   26 points

The following diagram will help you to classify and evaluate your symptoms:

Dimension of depression
Score

A	Mood disturbance	
B	Loss of hope	
C	Feelings of rejection	
D	Loss of enjoyment	
E	Feelings of guilt	
F	Need to be punished	
G	Self hatred	
H	Self condemnation	
I	Suicidal tendencies	
J	Tearfulness	
K	Irritability	
L	Disturbance of relationships	

M	Indecisiveness	☐
N	Negative self-image	☐
O	Incapacity for work	☐
P	Sleep disturbance	☐
Q	Tiredness	☐
R	Loss of appetite	☐
S	Weight loss	☐
T	Hypochondria	☐
U	Loss of libido	☐
TOTAL		☐

Copyright 1978 by Aaron T, Beck, M.D. Centre for Cognitive Therapy, Room 602, 133 South 63rd Street, Philadelphia, Pa, 19104

The Forms of Depression

Depression can occur in the most diverse forms (see Figure 7-1). These extend from illness which has a purely physical cause to depression occurring as a reaction to external circumstances (loss of a dear person or of other valued relations and things).

The diagram shows that in every depression there is an interplay between two components, namely the physical—biochemical (endogenous) component and the psychological—reactive (psychogenic) component.

The organic constituents of depression are most obvious. These occur as a result of brain damage, meningitis, interruptions of blood supply to the brain, etc. Severe depressions can also result from debilitating illness. A prolonged depressive condition will often follow a severe bout of influenza or a long course of hepatitis. In these cases we talk about a symptomatic depression.

By 'schizoaffective depression' psychiatrists understand those depressive conditions which occur within the context of a psychotic (for instance, schizophrenic) affliction (see chapter 9 to 11). This diagnosis can only be made after a prolonged period of observation. In any case, it covers severe forms of depression in which the patient's contact with reality is clearly disturbed.

I will deal with unipolar and bipolar depressions later. By a late depression we understand a severe depression which occurs in the later years of life and is partially caused by the ageing of the brain. It is more difficult to define the neurotic depression. These people suffer particularly from the emotional wounds which they have experienced through other people.

Oppressive experiences in childhood and youth are often put forward as the trigger for this kind of depression, but time will reveal that those who are affected generally find life more difficult and react with extreme sensitivity to both real and imaginary sickness. However, one does these patients an injustice by portraying their depression as simply a false or sinful reaction. The diagram shows that genetic factors also play a part here making it more difficult for the person affected to cope with the normal disappointments of life.

How Does Depression Come About?

There are many theories about the causes of depression.[5] I will consciously restrict myself in this chapter to informing the reader what is known within the current state of medical science, and what the pastoral counsellor can observe in dealing with depressive people.

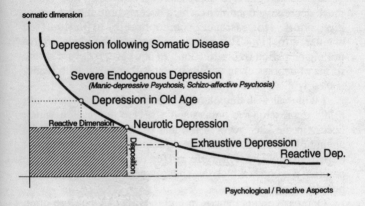

Figure 7-1

The Forms of Depression (After Kielholz)

In the outline above, the distinction between the individual forms of depression seems clear and unequivocal. However, inward and outward causes, soul and body, do not allow themselves to be separated as neatly and completely as we would like them to be. They have a mutual influence on one another. I have tried to present these connections in figure 7-2.

Figure 7-2

The Development of Depression

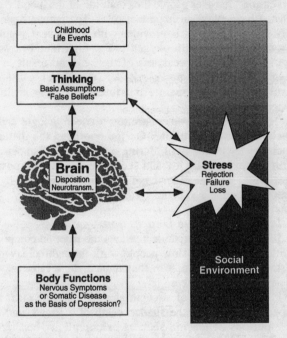

I have consciously placed the brain in the centre, because it is here that the processes which lead to depression are controlled. We have already looked at the miracle of the human brain (see chapter 3) and seen in the process the role played by biochemistry in the understanding of a psychological problem. Quite a lot of people have a moderate hereditary disorder in the metabolism of their brain (a so-called disposition) which makes them vulnerable to external pressures, so that when they come under stress, they are likely to react with a depression.

The body is closely bound up with the mind. Even in young people depressions are often accompanied by physical complaints. On the other hand, physical disorders may trigger depression. In older people the condition of the blood vessels and the heart plays an important role. The human brain can only function when it is provided with a sufficient supply of blood (and hence with oxygen). But high blood pressure, arteriosclerosis and weakness of the heart all result in less oxygen reaching the nerve cells . . . depression can be the result. With appropriate treatment it can completely disappear.

There is also a close connection between thought and the biochemistry of the brain. On the one hand the disturbed biochemistry of the brain during a depression dampens the ability to experience joy and see the world from a positive viewpoint. On the other hand it is also influenced by the person's thoughts and belief system.

Mild and Moderate Depression

In mild and moderate depressions the reaction component is often to the fore. How people work through bereavement or stress depends on the way they think and the value they put on particular experiences.

Physical reserves of strength also play an important role. Experiences such as the sudden death of a friend, and also long periods of tension such as examination pressures or marriage problems can so to speak 'eat at the nerves' and lead to an exhaustion of the supplies of biochemical substances in the brain. As a result a dark veil falls over the person's whole emotional life and they begin to see everything, themselves, their environment, their future, in a dark perspective. Situations of depressive exhaustion do not happen by accident. Often a depression is also to be understood as an alarm: 'Stop! You are overdoing it! You are expecting too much of yourself!' Or perhaps: 'Why can't you get the better of this misfortune? What are you allowing to rule your thoughts? What gives you your feeling of self-worth?' Even in the milder depressions it can be observed that negative thoughts can strengthen the depression. But Christian faith changes thinking to the positive. It fosters hope, comforts, encourages, and directs the gaze above. So faith can be a very real help in overcoming a depression.

The troubles of a depression snatch a person out of the daily round and make him think about the real meaning of his life.[6] So the crisis can also provide the chance for a new beginning.

Severe Endogenous Depression

In my work as a psychiatrist I am continually meeting people who become ill with the deepest depressions, far beyond the normal level, without any external cause. At any time about 1.3% of the population will be suffering from a severe depression. The risk of undergoing a severe depression at some time during the course of one's life lies at about 5–10%.

Those who are affected in this way have the impression that they have been suddenly, out of the blue, wrapped round with a gloomy fog of darkness of soul. 'Really, I have everything I could wish,' a lady patient told me: 'I have a dear husband and three bright children. Things are going well for us materially, and we have no cause for worry. We are both believers, and are active in our church. I can't understand why I have become so dejected, anxious and depressed.'

Another woman, who fell into a deep depression after the birth of her third child, complained: 'I should be happy about our baby, but I can only see myself as a failure. I could easily harm this child. It would be best if we were all dead.'

Mostly there is nothing to be found in their life history to account for a severe depression of this kind. Of course, these people have not gone through life experiencing only sunshine and happiness. Indeed, hardly anyone has an ideal, burden-free life behind them. But there is no relationship in these patients between the cause of the depression and their circumstances. Often there are other people among their relations who have suffered from 'melancholia' or who have taken their own life.

The condition is not only characterised by a depressed mood, but also by sleep disturbances and somatic complaints as they are described in tables 7-1 and 7-2. In these cases, the physician's first thought of an endogenous, biochemical cause for the depression.

The Course of Endogenous Depression

There are four possible courses that an endogenous depression can take. There may be one or more bouts of severe depression which may last weeks or even months, with in between, times in which the person affected lives, thinks and feels as normal. In this case the psychiatrist will talk about a mono-polar depression.

The other form of endogenous depression shows a wave pattern, not only below normality but also above it. The agonising depth is followed by a high which the patient experiences as a release from their unbearable situation. In this case we talk of a manic-depressive psychosis, or of a bipolar depression.

Finally, there are also chronic depressions. These last more than two years and respond only in an unsatisfactory way to medication.

It has been estimated that 10 to 20 per cent of depressions take a chronic course (8). These cases do not always consist of the worse depressive states. Even a moderate feeling of depression can be enormously oppressive, when you see no light at the end of the tunnel. Chronically depressive people often meet with little understanding from those around them, which drives them into the additional problem of loneliness.

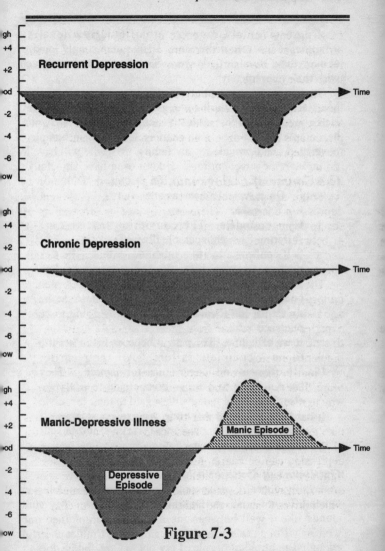

Figure 7-3

Various Courses of Depressive Syndromes

Depressive delusions are a particularly alienating symptom in a severe depression. Rather than simply looking at everything through dark spectacles, the patient loses touch with reality completely.

I can vividly remember an old man who stayed in the hospital for a period during a severe endogenous depression. He believed he had lost all his possessions. With a sad voice he complained to me: 'I've nothing left. I'm in complete poverty. I can't provide for my family. My wife will have to go through the streets in rags. I don't even have any clothes to wear myself. 'This condition is called 'Delusion of Poverty'. Other typical delusions are:

- Hypochondria. The conviction that you are suffering from an incurable illness.
- Self condemnation to a ridiculous extent. The sick person blames himself for having broken something, for which he must be punished. A man believes he has ruined the hospital because he didn't eat his food, and so now he is going to be punished for it.
- Ideas of failure. The patient believes his or her life to be a complete failure. All their earlier achievements no longer count for anything. They have nothing to offer in comparison to everyone else. They have failed with regard to their job, civic duties, etc., etc. A young woman complained 'I don't even know how a radio works. My life isn't worth living any more!'

Delusions of Guilt and Sinfulness

Finally, there is yet another form of depressive delusion which afflicts Christians: Delusions of sinfulness. 'My guilt stands like a wall between me and God' complained one woman. 'I'm a useless mother, I can't cook, I'm not cheerful enough, I'm afraid of people. I cry out to God, but he doesn't hear me. I try to cling on to a promise, but God can't accept a failure like me.'

There are people who have every reason for remorse and fall into a depression (usually a mild, and reactive one) as a result of genuine guilt. But in this case it was different. There wasn't a single remaining sin, even a really tiny one, which this woman hadn't already confessed umpteen times. Yet her 'sin' still towered before her like a gigantic mountain. When the milk boiled over she saw it as confirmation of her vileness. She lamented the terrible sin of not sending a card on time for her sister's birthday. This delusion has nothing to do with real conviction of sin. What we are faced with here is a pathological condition.

You may ask 'what can be done for someone who suffers from a depressive delusion? How can a man with a delusion of poverty be helped?' I will go over the therapy of depression systematically in the next chapter, but let me anticipate this by saying that it takes patience, lots of patience. Every attempt to reassure the patient that the opposite of their delusion is true leads to a reinforcement of the diseased ideas. However, usually, as the depression becomes less severe, the delusions also subside of their own accord.

In some cases such ideas may persist and may trouble the afflicted person into old age. These people will need a special degree of understanding and patient care by doctor and pastoral counsellor alike.

Mania: Flight From Joy to Elation

Emerging from the dark sea of melancholy is a powerful experience for any severe depressive. They will describe the change as 'like being unchained', indeed, 'like a new life'. Yet for many people, depression is followed by a swing into mania. This is characterised by a lightened mood,[10] increased drive and accelerated thought processes ('flights of fancy').

A woman wrote the following words at the beginning of her manic phase: 'I feel like nature itself at this moment. Progressing from its long winter sleep it sprouts from every tip and joint, sending out new buds. The birds trill and promise a new warm time to come . . . a new year, a spring with blossom, soft, green meadows with bubbling rivers and streams . . . '

Yet the joy soon turns into a nightmarish high-altitude flight. The same woman paid an enormous amount of money for a new wardrobe of clothes with strident colours, because her 'depressive clothes' no longer suited her new-found joy. With her unbounded creative energy, she started getting up at four in the morning, and didn't go to bed until one. She wasn't at all bothered that the loud music from her apartment bothered her neighbours. In her elation she lost all feeling of aloofness and got herself involved with men who were complete strangers. The once withdrawn, decent and quiet lady spoke in a loud voice, and called her friends at all hours of the day and night to tell them how good things were going for her. In the end her behaviour became such a burden for people around her that she had to be admitted to a psychiatric unit.

The manic phase is thus the reverse side of the depression. Where before there was a lack of energy, the sick person now shows almost superhuman energy. Where before he was controlled by the worries and cares of life, he no longer sees any problems or dangers. Where before he withdrew into his shell, now he wants to embrace the whole world. Where before he struggled under his guilt and sinfulness, now he is incapable of experiencing guilt and sin, even though his behaviour frequently transgresses moral boundaries.

Relatives experience enormous suffering through their manic spouse or child. Parents often don't know any way to help, other than to ban their son from the house 'until he comes to his senses'. Marriages are frequently shattered by the manic phase of a partner. The wife of a manic husband once wrote to me: 'I find it such a torment, I don't know what to do.' What I'd really like to do is to make a final break with him and leave him. But should I do that? All the time I keep praying and asking the Lord for a miracle, and for him to make things clear to me, but somehow I'm always far from it . . . '

You have now read a lot about the forms, causes and the course of endogenous depression. You may be asking yourself, what hope is there for severe depressives? Is there any hope for the overwound manic person? Is there hope for their suffering relatives? I would like to answer with a cautious 'yes', and in the next chapter I shall look into the pastoral care of depressive conditions and the various possibilities for therapy.

CHAPTER EIGHT

THE THERAPY AND PASTORAL CARE OF SEVERE DEPRESSION

Depression does not have to be an unchangeable fate. The doctor and pastoral counsellor can offer hope even to the severe depressive. Even when, in the valley of the shadow, a depressive person sees no way out, he needs to be confidently reassured that there are passable routes out of depression, and that indeed, the road through the darkness can even bless and help him in his personal growth.

In the previous chapter I explained that many factors work together to contribute to the development of a depression. In the same way, when it comes to therapy, we need to tackle the suffering on different levels. We have established four important areas in the development of a depression:

- Thinking, or a person's belief system
- External stress (loss, rejection, disappointment, etc.)
- Physical reactions and disturbances
- The biochemistry of the brain

Correspondingly, the therapy of depression can be divided into four sections:

1. Counselling
2. Practical help and relief
3. General motivation and treatment of physical symptoms
4. Medication

These forms of therapy have a mutually intensifying effect on each other. No one approach should be taken without the others. It is possible to do without medication in mild depressions, but the doctor should always be consulted in more severe situations.

A depression is not only a crisis of emotion, but also a crisis of belief.[1] For this reason, pastoral input is indispensable and helpful alongside the medical treatment, provided the pastoral counsellor knows the points to be careful and where his limitations lie.

Helps for Counselling

Helping severely depressive people makes considerable demands on the patience and empathetic skills of both the doctor and the pastoral counsellor. These qualities are indispensable for counselling depressives. I have compiled a list of seven points to which attention should be given when counselling them. These are as follows:[2]

1. Accept the depressive person in their sickness and trouble, and show them your readiness to accompany them through this difficult time.
2. Talk over the patient's life history with him or her. Explore with them the experiences which triggered the depression. Give them the opportunity to empty their heart.
3. Stress the hopeful outcome of the suffering. Most depressions die away after a certain time.
4. Explain the different possibilities for treatment, and send the patient with a severe depression to their G.P.

5. Encourage the counsellee and speak about God's love, even at times when he or she feels little of it. There are many helpful passages to be found in the Psalms, as well as in many scripture promises.[3]

6. Prepare the counsellee for occasional mood swings. I often tell my patients, 'The road out of depression is full of pot-holes, but it leads up to the light.'

7. Be patient! Set one goal for therapy at a time, so that the patient keeps having little successes. Don't expect too much at once. Remember, depressed people are often so hemmed in, that they are scarcely aware of pastoral conversations, and can take in only a little at a time.

Avoidable Mistakes

There are a number of concealed traps and pitfalls in conversation with depressive people which it is necessary to avoid. Most mistakes are related to the following points:[4]

DEMANDING 'PULL YOURSELF TOGETHER': Depressed people are already placing themselves under a massive burden of self-imposed obligations, and suffering as a result of their supposed failure. It is of little help to them for the pastoral counsellor to add to this pressure, backing it up with verses from the Bible. You can't simply order someone to be happy!

SENDING THEM ON HOLIDAY OR ON LEAVE: Even in their familiar surroundings, it is difficult for patients to make contact with people, enjoy beauty and fill their day on their own initiative. But that is exactly what will be required of them on holiday. It will trap the sick person by overburdening him.

ALLOWING THEM TO TAKE IMPORTANT DECISIONS: Often during a depression a patient is not capable of properly evaluating his situation. He sees everything through 'dark glasses'. His problems tower over him like a mountain, and he underestimates his abilities. Decisions taken during a depressive phase will often be recognised afterwards as wrong, and regretted.

ASSERTING 'THINGS ARE ALREADY BETTER!': It is often difficult for the carer to understand that for a depressed person things are the same week after week. You will often find yourself trying to encourage them with cheap words, but the result is to leave them feeling they haven't been taken seriously. It is better to recognise that they are still going through the 'valley of the shadow', and speak the presence of God into the midst of their darkness (5).

CASTING DOUBT ON DELUSIONAL IDEAS: Many people suffer from the most severe delusions of guilt and failure. No argument can move them away from these delusions and each attempt to assert the opposite leads to a fresh confirmation of the delusion. What is needed here is to be patient and convince the sufferer through the way they are personally valued by the pastoral counsellor and the grace of God. I often encourage my patients with the thought: 'Even when our conscience accuses us and pronounces us guilty, we should trust that God is greater than our conscience. He knows us absolutely as we are (6)'. Then I close the conversation without further discussion and give them a new appointment. The sick person needs time to digest what he has heard, even if he still carries a lot of 'ifs' and 'buts' about it.

ENTERING TOO FULLY INTO THE DEPRESSIVE CONDITION: The depressive person is often completely imprisoned by his cares and fears. There is great danger in allowing yourself to be drawn into this twilight world and completely forgetting to ask what he is still capable of and what gives him security. We find the right balance in the Psalms. Time and time again the divine 'nevertheless' breaks into the personal trouble of the one praying and directs his gaze above.[7]

MAKING TOO MANY SPIRITUAL DEMANDS: God's Word should be like salt in a tasty meal. Without reference to God's promises, pastoral care is reduced to idle chit-chat. But an abundance of words from scripture which lacks relationship to every day life and to the depressed person's suffering, is like a salty concentrate. Indeed it can add to the sick person's feelings to such an extent that he becomes unable to receive God's Word and feels condemned.

When studying the Bible intensively, a severe depressive will tend only to read the thoughts which are endorsed by his darkened perspective on things. The most beautiful promises will only awaken in him the thought 'This no longer applies to a sinner like me!' and unbelief will grow.

For this reason, I deliberately advise depressed people not to immerse themselves very deeply in the Bible any more, but to read just one verse each day, preferably with an explanation in a devotional book. God's love does not depend on the number of chapters you read and how many hours you spend in prayer. God holds us in His hand, even when we lack the power to hold on to Him.

PRACTICAL HELP AND ENCOURAGEMENT: Counselling alone is not enough in many cases. The pastoral counsellor must be ready to climb down from lofty spiritual conversation into the 'lower regions' of everyday life and give very practical help. It may be necessary to relieve an over-burdened housewife of some of her responsibilities or a depressive husband will need to be encouraged to hand his committee responsibilities over to someone else until he is on his feet again.

It is often important to call in relatives and to discuss with them how the sick person can be relieved of some of their burdens. So for instance a female patient's mother may come in two days a week to do the washing and ironing while the husband helps a little more with the housework. In this way the burden is shared and rests on several shoulders.

On the road to health the depressed person will need to be slowly reactivated. Work out a daily schedule with him and encourage him to take part in small activities. Regular walks and some kind of sport stimulate the circulation and so have a positive effect on depression. In time the depressed person will begin to take up new responsibilities for himself once again. The more the numbness of depression is released, the freer he or she will be to be active and enjoy achieving things again.

HELP THROUGH MEDICATION: For about thirty years now, medicine has made use of drugs which have a pronounced influence on depression. It is understood that they effect the nerve connections and lead to a restoration of the brain's biochemistry. However, many questions are still unresolved and need further research.

Not every depressive needs medication. You can do without medication in slight to moderate depressions, if the person affected receives regular help through counselling. Studies have shown that in these cases the complaint can be healed with equal rapidity with or without antidepressants.[8]

The use of antidepressants also has little effect on certain people whose depression is caused by arteriosclerosis.

In severe depressions, however, modern drugs are an enormous help, undergirding counselling sessions with the sick person.

Often patients are built up at the start by medication to a point where they are ready to receive counselling from a doctor or pastoral counsellor. The doctor will hope, through using anti-depressant drugs, to achieve the following goals:

- release from inward nervousness and tension
- reduction of crippling feelings of anxiety
- lightening of the melancholy mood
- re-establishment of adequate sleep

- improvement in the patient's ability to cope with everyday burdens and trials
- prevention of any relapse of recurring endogenous depression and manic-depressive psychoses.

Nowadays a broad range of antidepressants is available to help in the achievement of these aims.[9] Which drug the doctor chooses will depend on the situation which he observes in the patient. Is he suffering from restlessness, anxiety and insomnia? Or is she feeling weak and lethargic? Is she overwhelmed by feelings of sadness, or complaining that her feelings are totally numbed? In each case the doctor will prescribe a corresponding drug, either a sedative, an antidepressant or a stimulant. The drug will not begin to fully take effect until something like five to ten days into the treatment. Nevertheless, the medication should be taken at regular intervals in order to facilitate the build up of the drug in the brain which is needed for it to be effective.

I often explain this situation to my patients with the help of the following analogy: 'Imagine a reservoir, where the dam has been broken. The water has run out . . . the reservoir is empty. In the same way, you are suffering from an exhaustion of your resources of physical and emotional strength. The antidepressants are now filling the hole in the dam, but it will take time for enough water to build up to drive the turbines again.'

However it often makes little sense to just wait a whole week for the drug to take affect. That is why the antidepressant is often supplemented with tranquillisers and sleeping tablets. Patients are enormously thankful when at last they are able to sleep properly and their inner tension is relaxed.

The side effects of antidepressants vary according to the drug and the dosage. Most patients take the prescribed drug without any problems Others quickly become accustomed to it and stop experiencing the side effects. A little constipation and dryness of the mouth is a small price to pay for a lightening of the depression. However, if the side-effects continue to be very distressing, it will be necessary to change to a different remedy which may produce fewer undesired effects.

LITHIUM[10] plays a particular part in the therapy of depressions. This simple mineral salt can prevent a relapse in cases of recurrent severe depression and manic-depressive psychosis. The reason may very possibly be that Lithium stabilises the ability of the nerves to conduct electricity. Many people who previously suffered from regularly recurring depressive and manic phases are today, thanks to Lithium, free from trouble and able to live and work normally.

Personality Change Through Antidepressants?

I am asked again and again by both lay people and theologians, whether antidepressants and tranquillisers alter a person's personality, and whether on these grounds they should be rejected from a Christian point of view. From my observation, I would say that exactly the opposite is true. It is depression which alters the personality and leads to despondency, despair, nervousness and anxiety which the afflicted person would otherwise never have known. The medication helps him to the point where he thinks and feels once again as he did in the days when he was healthy.

Many patients complain that they experience a 'deadening' of their feelings while taking antidepressants. But often it is not easy to discern whether the calming effect is due to the medication, or due to the depression itself.

Personally, I am convinced that modern psychopharmacy can be a valuable help in conquering depression, even for Christians, if it is supplemented by regular counselling and practical help.

Recognising Suicidal Tendencies

This chapter about the treatment and care of depressive people would be incomplete were I not to refer to the recognition and treatment of suicidal tendencies.

Thoughts about death and suicide are part of the picture of a severe depression. They become a particular danger for depressed people who feel excessively hemmed in and isolated. To begin with, they may simply long to be able to sleep and not wake up again. But then they start to think more and more about how to end their life, and if the net of hopelessness is pulled closer together it often happens that the thoughts begin to actively control them, so strongly that they no longer know how to resist them.

For many Christians it is not easy to give expression to such thoughts. They are afraid of how their fellow Christians will react, expecting to be condemned 'because a Christian doesn't have any thought of suicide'. A few pastoral counsellors regard such thoughts as signs of a lack of devotion to God, or even as evidence indicating demonic influence in the afflicted person. But this is exactly the kind of attitude which can drive a person deeper into hopelessness. For this reason it is important to recognise suicidal tendencies quickly, if effective counselling is to be given to the depressed person. The following questions can help in this:[11]

SUICIDAL TENDENCY Have you ever thought of taking your life?

PREPARATION How would you do it? Have you already made preparations? (The more concrete the idea, the greater the risk).

COMPULSIVE THOUGHTS Do you think about it of your own choice, or do the thoughts force themselves on you, even when you don't welcome them? (Thoughts which press in on someone passively are more dangerous).

WARNINGS Have you already talked about your intentions with someone else? (Always take warnings seriously!)

RESTRICTION Have your interests, thoughts and social contacts become more reduced and restricted?

AGGRESSION Do you have feelings of aggression against anyone, which you are forcibly suppressing? (such suppressed feelings can be directed against one's own person.)

There is a great deal of help to be gained from a book by Bill Blackburn, which deals with the subject from a Christian point of view. He enters in a very sympathetic way into the difficulties of those who are afflicted, and also the problems of their relatives and those who care for them. ('*What you should know about suicide*')[12] I would only want to add a few pieces of advice from a medical point of view. The following table shows the risk factors for suicide in depressive patients:

Table 8-1

When is There a Danger of Suicide?[14]

A *EARLY INDICATIONS OF SUICIDE*
  1. Previous suicide attempts and indications of suicidal tendencies
  2. History of suicide among family or other contacts
  3. Direct or indirect suicide threats
  4. Concrete plans or preparations for a suicide
  5. 'Uncanny calmness' after previous unrest and talk of suicide

6.   Dreams about self-destruction, falling or
     catastrophes.

*B PARTICULARLY DANGEROUS MEDICAL
SITUATIONS*
1.   Onset or tailing off of a depressive phase
2.   Signs of anxiety or agitation
3.   Prolonged disturbance of sleep
4.   Biological crisis periods (puberty, childbirth,
     menopause)
5.   Severe feelings of guilt or rejection
6.   Prolonged or incurable illness
7.   Hypochondria
8.   Alcoholism or drug addiction.

C ENVIRONMENTAL FACTORS
1.   Broken family relationships in childhood
2.   Absence or loss of human contact (loneliness,
     loss of 'roots', disappointment in love.)
3.   Redundancy, retirement, financial worries
4.   Absence or loss of supportive religious
     relationships.

Helping People at Risk From Suicidal Tendencies

The inexperienced helper is often too inhibited to voice
thoughts about suicide. But these impulses can become
stronger precisely as a result of this embarrassed silence. The
first principle for dealing with suicidal people is thus:

1. *GIVE VOICE TO THOUGHTS ABOUT SUICIDE.*
   Talking naturally about his wish to die will make it
   easier for the counsellee to express his innermost
   troubles and worries. The burden will be shared
   and preventive measures can be discussed.
2. *ASK QUESTIONS WHICH PROBE BEYOND THE
   HOPELESSNESS.* Suicide is only an option for a
   person who can see no other escape. Reviewing

the situation through the counsellor's eyes can raise the question: 'Is my situation really so hopeless?' The tiniest glimmer of hope can persuade the suicidal person to at least postpone taking their life for the time being.

3. *A STRONG RELATIONSHIP BETWEEN THE PASTORAL COUNSELLOR AND THE PATIENT* is extremely important during a suicidal crisis. The feeling of being supported and taken seriously can weaken suicidal thoughts. You can extract a promise from the depressive person not to attempt suicide, at least until after the next counselling session. In addition you can offer him the possibility of phoning every time thoughts of suicide start to come. In an emergency there are telephone counselling services which offer the opportunity to talk with a trained helper at any time, day or night. In Britain the 'Samaritans' provide this service and the number, which varies in each area, can be found in the local telephone directory. The equivalent service in some countries can be obtained by dialling a particular number nationwide.

Emergency calls like this are not always easy for the pastoral counsellor. I well remember an evening when the telephone rang about ten o'clock. A young woman was on the line whom I had already been helping for a long time through a severe depression. 'Doctor, I can't go on any longer' she said in a toneless voice. 'The thought of killing myself is getting stronger and stronger. I can't resist any more. But I just wanted to ask you before I do it, can you help me?

Don't think for a moment that I sat by the telephone and gave sound advice in a calm and professional way. I sweated and prayed inwardly for God to give me the wisdom to know how to help that woman. After a few minutes I noticed that the person I was talking to was calmer and in the end we managed to arrange for someone to call and see her that evening so she wouldn't be completely on her own. The telephone conversation, with God's help, had broken the spell of her suicidal thoughts.

Such telephone calls take a lot out of you, but the committed pastoral counsellor must be ready to share this burden as much as lies in him.

4. *CONSULT WITH RELATIVES AND FRIENDS* A person who is strongly suicidal should never be left on their own. Admission to a psychiatric unit is not always necessary. In shorter crises their parents or partner can be asked . . . in consultation with the patient . . . to watch over the suicidal person and give him or her more attention. This constant supervision will become too much of a burden for the relatives if the risk of suicide is serious or prolonged. Then the courageous decision has to be taken to admit them for intensive supervision and treatment in hospital.

5. *GIVE THERAPY AT FREQUENT INTERVALS* Give the suicidal person an appointment to talk further at the earliest date possible. Encourage them to have medical treatment from a doctor with drugs which will calm them and lead to re-establishment of normal sleep patterns.

6. *ADMISSION TO HOSPITAL* When the measures described above are insufficient, a stay in hospital will be unavoidable.

In acute crises a psychiatric unit has much to offer every patient, the believer included: additional possibilities for therapy, increased attention and supervision, and a refuge from the fears, and life-situations which are felt to be unbearable. These measures can prevent the worst from happening in

the majority of cases. Nevertheless, we always
have to live with a residue of uncertainty.
Unfortunately, a psychiatric unit cannot give the
ultimate security. It comes as a shock to the
pastoral counsellor and the psychiatric social
worker alike when they experience their
powerlessness to help as, in spite of all efforts, a
patient succeeds in taking their own life. Often the
pastoral counsellor will as a result carry wounds of
his own which will take a long while to heal.

Help for the Pastoral Counsellor

A client's depression has an effect on the pastoral
counsellor. It is his or her duty to help the depressed person,
and he feels in part responsible for him. If as so often
happens the pastoral counsellor becomes infected by the
hopelessness and helplessness of the client, the counselling
sessions become an increasing burden. For this reason I
would like to conclude this chapter by giving some advice as
to how this outcome can be avoided.

1. Keep the facts about the depression in view! Don't
   allow yourself to be drawn along by the patient's
   temporary hopelessness.
2. Be on guard against untrue, depressive ideas in
   yourself, as well as in the patient. Are your
   thoughts always in tune with the Bible and with
   reality?
3. Learn to counter the client's suffering with a
   healthy objectivity. For instance, just accept tears
   as signs of inner distress. Consciously limit the
   length of each counselling session, otherwise it
   will be too taxing for you as well as the sick
   person.
4. Don't accept responsibility for the thoughts,
   feelings and behaviour of your client. They have
   to carry this responsibility themselves. You can

certainly give them a push here and there, but change in the patient has to come about through God's grace (and according to His timing).

5. Don't set too high goals for therapy. Keep reminding yourself that helping depressive people takes a lot of patience and always involves set-backs.

6. Have the courage to face your own helplessness and talk with another pastoral counsellor about your difficulties in caring for a depressive person.

7. Take enough time for personal fellowship with God and with your family. Nurture contact with friends and enjoy time for hobbies, sport or music.

By far the greatest encouragement for any doctor or pastoral counsellor is to hear from ex-patients about how they survived their depression. The inward brokenness of a severe depression often leads to a deeper relationship with God, and the rebuilding of a faith which proved itself even in the time of trouble.

A woman with a prolonged depression recently said to me: 'I wouldn't have wanted to miss this time. God broke my old, proud nature and directed my gaze back towards Him. I have nothing in this world that I can rely on. But He endures for ever. Sometimes I am afraid, at the beginning of a new depressive phase, that my clear, certain faith will be darkened again. Yet I know God comes with me, even when my path leads through another dark valley.'

CHAPTER NINE

SCHIZOPHRENIA - AN OVERVIEW

No other illness provokes so much controversy as schizophrenia. Its varied forms make it hard to understand, indeed, many people find it rather repulsive and scary. Physical illnesses are much easier to understand and deal with. The horrors of previous centuries, such as the plague, are now reduced to the status of common infectious fevers. Even lay people understand nowadays how physical illnesses come about and how they can be treated.

With schizophrenia it is different. The sick person's strange behaviour, the voices they hear, the fears they express, do not immediately point to a disorder of a physical organ. In spite of costly research we are still faced here by many unsolved riddles. Schizophrenia was first identified as a separate illness at the turn of the century. The German psychiatrist *Kraepelin* talked about a 'dementia praecox', an early dementia. *Eugen Bleuler*, senior consultant of the 'Burgholzli' University hospital in Zurich was the first to describe and list the diverse symptoms of this peculiar complaint. His name for the illness was 'schizophrenia'—the split mind.

The name was new, but not the illness. Schizophrenia is not confined to our own age. Time and time again, history leaves us descriptions of people who manifested the typical disorders which we label 'schizophrenia'. Equally, schizophrenia is not confined to particular geographical areas. It occurs in every land and nation, among all races and social classes. And it also occurs among believing Christians. Their fellow Christians often have difficulty understanding the changes which take place in those who are affected. How is it possible for their thought, feelings and behaviour to be so deeply disturbed? How can the situation come about that someone feels they are being followed by the secret service, sleeps only on the floor, because they are afraid of radiation, and feels they are constantly guided by voices?

In recent years schizophrenic people have become especially favourite patients of mine. It has been my privilege to walk with them and their relatives on their path through illness. Time and time again I have been amazed by their heroic struggle . . . both the struggle with their illness, and with their incomplete understanding of the world around them. I am writing this chapter for them, to moderate the injustice to which they are still continually subjected in modern society, inclined as it is towards success and normality.

Definitions and Statistics

Schizophrenia belongs to the group of illnesses known as psychoses. This term comprises severe disorders, which are recognisable by abnormal experience and behaviour as well as marked alteration of the personality, leading to the loss of the normal capacity for work. The person affected is no longer able to separate external events from their personal perceptions. Psychoses can last for a few hours or for years. They can be slight, or lead to a complete breakdown of personality. Psychoses include:

- organic psychoses (triggered by toxins, for e.g. drugs or infections such as syphilis)
- transitory reactions to stressful experiences
- the results of severe deterioration of the brain in old age
- manic-depressive illnesses
- schizophrenia.

In this chapter I will deal with schizophrenia. The other disorders may be mentioned here and there, but not fully described. The interested reader should consult text-books of psychiatry for further information.[1]

Schizophrenia is a comparatively common disorder. About half the patients who require admission to psychiatric hospitals suffer from it. Two statistics will give an idea of its frequency.

0.4% of the population suffer with symptoms of schizophrenia (acute or chronic) on any particular day. For comparison about 15 to 20 per cent are depressive on any particular day, and about 12% suffer from symptoms of a neurosis.

Schizophrenia affects 1 in 100 people in their lifetime. Every year there are 6000 new cases in Britain alone. Schizophrenia has an irregular hereditary pattern. Table 9-1 shows the risk of suffering from schizophrenia when another member of the family is already a sufferer.

TABLE 9-1

Probability of inherited schizophrenia
- If one parent is schizophrenic: 10%
- If one brother or sister is schizophrenic: 10%
- If both parents are schizophrenic: 20-40%
- If an identical twin is schizophrenic: 50%
- If a second degree relative (Uncle, nephew, cousin) is schizophrenic: 3%

These figures may be disturbing, but if we look at them another way, it means that even if a mother who suffers with schizophrenia had ten children, statistically, only one would suffer with the same disorder. All the same, in such families we often observe an increased incidence of other psychological disorders, which point to an underlying nervous weakness.

When May the Diagnosis of Schizophrenia be Established?

Today the diagnosis of schizophrenia is made with discernment. At an earlier stage in America every kind of conspicuous behaviour and transitory psychosis was labelled as schizophrenia, but for several years now strict criteria have been required for this diagnosis to be made.[2] Yet even for experienced psychiatrists it is difficult to be accurate in borderline cases, particularly at the start of an illness. Often it is better just to speak of an 'adolescent crisis, or simply a 'psychosis'.

Three phases are distinguished in the course of a schizophrenic illness which are described more fully in table 9-2.

A   Prodroma phase   (gradual deterioration)
B   Active phase   (acute symptoms)
C   Residual phase   (stable situation)

TABLE 9-2

Criteria for Diagnosis of Schizophrenia

DURATION: Total duration at least 6 months. Various durations are possible for the individual phases.

ONSET: Before the age of 45 years.

A.   PRODROMAL PHASE:

Obvious deterioration in comparison with earlier level of ability (performance at work; social relationships; care for personal appearance and hygiene). At least two of the symptoms listed below, which are not due to a disturbance in mood or to a psychoactive substance.

Symptoms During the Initial and Residual Phases:

1. Social isolation or withdrawal

2. Marked impairment of work, home life or studies
3. Marked peculiar behaviour (e.g. collecting rubbish, hoarding rotting food, uninhibited behaviour . . .)
4. Marked neglect of hygiene and grooming
5. Apathetic, shallow or unconventional expression of feelings
6. Wandering, vague, over-elaborate or circumstantial speech
7. Odd beliefs or magical thinking, influencing behaviour and inconsistent with cultural norms. Feeling of being influenced or being able to influence others, imagining significant connections between unrelated things or events.
8. Experience of abnormal perception, e.g. repeated illusions of the presence of an invisible person or power which cannot be experienced by others.

B. ACTIVE PHASE
At least one of the following characteristic features:

1. Bizarre delusions (essentially and obviously absurd and with no possible basis in reality.) For instance, feeling of being influenced or having special powers, or being able to read people's thoughts, or having thoughts extracted from your brain.
2. Delusions related to the body, delusions of greatness, religious, nihilistic or other delusions.
3. Delusions of jealousy or being pursued, combined with hallucinations.
4. Hearing voices (either commenting on the afflicted person's behaviour, or talking among themselves).
5. Distracted thought, marked tendency for mental connections to be seen much more loosely, marked illogicality of thought, and pronounced deterioration of verbal abilities, if this occurs

together with at least one of the following features:

- apathetic, shallow or unconventional expression of feelings
- delusions or hallucinations
- catatonic or otherwise severely disorganised behaviour.

C.   RESIDUAL PHASE

(Residual = remaining).   At least two of the symptoms listed under A, which continue after an active phase of the illness and are not caused by a bad mood or by drugs.

Forms and Cause of Schizophrenia

It is not always easy to define individual symptoms of schizophrenia.   Currently, the tendency is to distinguish three forms of schizophrenia which are briefly describable as follows:

1.   HEBEPHRENIA (or disorganised schizophrenia):

Onset in youth, childish, silly behaviour, breakdown of personality, often aimless, clearly reduced ability to work,

Example: 17 year old Sylvia from a well-ordered family is experiencing various pressures.   She is in the middle of the end of year exams, in her catering course, on top of which her friendship with a young man has just been broken off.   Her personality changes increasingly.   She becomes obsessed and pesters her ex-boyfriend day and night with telephone calls. She feels sad, but laughs constantly and without reason. When she is working she does everything wrong.   In the end she runs away from it and spends the night in the open air in the pouring rain.   This leads to her being admitted to hospital.

2.   CATATONIC SCHIZOPHRENIA:

Marked disturbances of movement are to the fore (e.g. remaining for hours in an unusual posture for an agitated state).

Example: A 35 year-old mechanic, Mr. F., is intensely occupied in building his own home. Tensions with the architect lead to a court case. Mr. F. becomes unable to sleep, stops going to work, and spends all his time brooding over his building plans. One morning his wife finds him sitting at the table as if petrified. He suddenly utters the words 'watermain', and knocks meaningfully on the table. The condition normalises itself with the help of medication after a three week stay in hospital.

3. PARANOID SCHIZOPHRENIA:

The person affected suffers from a pronounced system of delusion (delusion of grandeur, delusion of being an inventor, delusion of being followed).

Example: 22 year-old painter and decorator Thomas K is convinced that four years ago he discovered the laser-beam. With the aid of a magnifying glass he has now developed a 'computerised video-magnifier' as well as a 'photo-driven helicopter', which the police can use for tracking criminals. When he touches the table with his finger-tips, he can store his feelings on the surface of the wood. He spends more than £3,000 on tools and instruments to continue developing his inventions. He makes a lot of mistakes at work, because he continually feels distracted by murmuring voices and laser beams.

It is not always immediately possible to categorise a condition under one of these forms of schizophrenia. In the hospital we observe the most diverse mixed forms for which there are yet other names. Two of these are named here: an insidious schizophrenia with few symptoms will be labelled as 'schizophrenia simplex'. If schizophrenic symptoms are combined with severe mood changes (deep depression or mania) we talk of a schizoaffective psychosis.

The Course of Schizophrenia

Recent research into the course of schizophrenia has

shown that the prognosis for this illness is considerably better than has generally been thought.[3]

There is no cause for unnecessary pessimism. Basically we can observe three possible courses for the development of schizophrenia, as outlined in Figure 9-1.

1) Single episode with no repetition
2) Repeated attacks with resultant disability
3) Chronic deterioration leading to a severe residual state

Figure 9-1

Possible Courses Taken By Schizophrenia

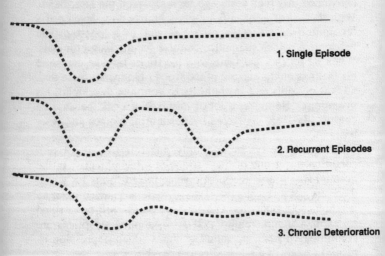

1. Single Episode

2. Recurrent Episodes

3. Chronic Deterioration

1) In about 20 per cent of cases, an episode of schizophrenia does not lead to any further relapse,

even when these people experience heightened nervousness under stress. Particularly favourable indications are:

- normal adjustment before the illness
- sudden onset with many symptoms
- relatively good health after an attack phase
- harmonious conditions at home
- motivation towards regular treatment.

2) In about 60 per cent of patients, further attacks occur over the years. In between times these people live normal lives, even if, in retrospect, they are less able to cope with stress. Unfortunately their ability is somewhat reduced after each attack. A so-called residual or defective condition remains, which makes it more difficult for them to operate effectively at home, at school, or in the workplace. It is not uncommon for them to have to come to terms with a more modest goal in their career. This is not completely negative. I think of Beattie, a nurse who could only work to 70 per cent of her capability after a psychotic attack. After a further attack she was transferred to work at a convalescent home, where the demands made on her were less stringent. Every few years, when she was under unusual stress, she experienced a short crisis. Once it was to do with a relationship with a man. Another time an exhausting trip to Tunisia. She would feel better after a short stay in hospital. In her lovely, sympathetic, way she was a great blessing to many patients.

3) With the final 20 per cent of patients a complete personality breakdown eventually develops. Even under medication, they are not free from delusions and hallucinations. They are no longer able to

work. Often they are incapable of caring for themselves and living on their own. Because of their bizarre behaviour and marked lack of personal hygiene and grooming they become such a burden for their relatives that they require continual supervision in a psychiatric hospital.

The Psychosis as a 'Jamming' Station

The research of the last few years has shown that at the roots of all forms of schizophrenia lie common disturbances which especially impair the thought processes of the brain.[4] The other difficulties, such as altered and suppressed expression of feeling, social withdrawal, alteration of self-awareness, delusions, the senses playing tricks on them and motor disturbances, all follow from these disorders.[5]

What do we mean by 'distracted thought'? Someone who has never experienced the mental changes in a person who is undergoing an attack of schizophrenia can hardly imagine it. I vividly remember a 28-year-old woman, who developed a psychosis in connection with giving birth. At her admission interview, communication was barely possible. Her thoughts were like a broken stained glass window. Word fragments sparkled out, but they didn't fit together, and no longer formed a picture for the person looking on.

'I feel like I am an N. N for necessity. But I can't get it, because there is an F in the way. I can't tell you what an F is just now. I don't feel myself any more. The dot in my i is missing. (She knocks her head pointedly to indicate the dot.) The word 'marriage' has a special meaning, M for Marriage. If you take the M away there are three marks that look into the sky. That's what I tripped over. Look at the R in marriage. I fell down the R. I fell down deep . . . a long, long way, until I came to the doctor. He gave me a tablet (the patient draws an R on the table, then an arrow underneath, and finally a circle to represent the tablet) and here I was almost blown up.'

This fragmentation of the thoughts is often underscored by a massive disturbance affecting handwriting. Figure 9-2 shows an example of the handwriting of a man during a psychotic attack, before he was treated with medication. Notice the uneven lines, the broken sentences, the desperate attempt to make himself understood to the reader.

Those afflicted in this way are themselves aware that they can't connect their thoughts any longer, especially when too many impressions crowd in at once. 'My thoughts greet one another, but I don't know which one I should shake by the hand', is how one young woman expressed it. Often at the height of an attack sick people will become so absorbed with what is going on in their mind, that they are unable to turn their attention to another person, let alone apply themselves to a job. They seem completely 'gone out'. But you do these people an injustice to describe them as 'insane'. They are just incapable, for a certain time, of processing the impressions that bombard them from within and without, in a normal way.

Figure 7-1

The Handwriting of a 35-year-old German Man During an Acute Psychosis

Many aspects of their personality remain healthy. The healthy person is not lost, merely hidden behind the psychosis which takes the front stage. The psychosis often 'jams' the 'programme' so persistently that it can only be understood in a fragmentary way. It is precisely those people who depend on the orderly processes of their mind for a career, who suffer most when they can no longer make use of their ability. It is much more difficult for them to find suitable employment, than it is for a simple factory worker who remains capable of routine work after the acute phase has subsided.

How Does Schizophrenia Develop?

This question has troubled researchers for decades. Every year thousands of articles and books appear addressing this subject. Research is being carried out into many areas, from biochemistry to behavioural studies. The workings of our brain are so complex that so far we have only been able to propose models which may help us understand schizophrenia. Nevertheless, a number of main guidelines have been established, which can be supported by extensive research. The Swiss psychiatrist, Professor Ciompi has summarised these factors in a model (figure 9-3) which I will briefly describe as follows:[6]

The hereditary influence can be regarded as established by the studies that have been made of twins and adoptive children.[7] Schizophrenic people obviously have an inherited weak point in the metabolism of the brain. The influence of the environment in turn chips away at this weakness.[8] A picture emerges of a vulnerable personality which is less able to cope under stress. This in turn can be recognised by the following characteristics, among others:[9]

- 'Ego weakness' and sensitivity
- Abnormal anxiousness
- Reduced ability to experience joy (anhedony)
- Reduced ability to express feelings
- Withdrawal into an inner world (introversion)

- Reduced independence
- Difficulty in making relationships
- Defective performance at work or in school
- Limited capacity to process information

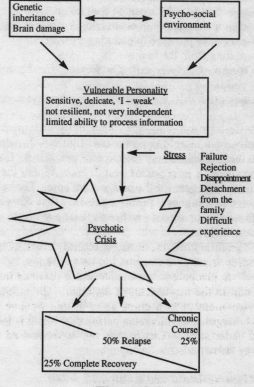

Figure 9-3

A Model for the Understanding of Schizophrenia (After Ciompi, 1981)

When this personality comes under pressure or stress, it ceases to be able to cope with the thoughts, feelings and responsibilities which arise, and a 'nervous breakdown' occurs, a psychotic crisis such as has already been described. The triggers for this can be very diverse:

- failure (e.g. at school)
- rejection (e.g. by a person they love)
- disappointment (e.g. in attaining a career goal)
- excessive pressure (e.g. during a divorce)
- parting from the family
- a new role (e.g. military service, the birth of a child)
- any other difficult experience (e.g. bereavement)

The relationship between vulnerability and stress can be presented in a simple diagram (see figure 4-2, page 65).[10] Notice the distinction between triggers and causes. If a bridge collapses when a lorry passes over it, the weight of the lorry is only the final trigger for the bridge's collapse. The cause will lie in some weakness, perhaps the fact that for years the pillars of the bridge have been rusting without anyone noticing. It is the same with the experiences which lead to the onset of schizophrenia, however stressful they may seem. The problem is not in the first instance with the experiences themselves, but with the way in which a person responds to those experiences. How many feelings of guilt, how many accusations, and how many empty clichés could be avoided by this way of viewing things! This is especially valid with regard to the religious triggers of schizophrenia, of which I shall speak later.

Schizophrenic Phenomena and Their Explanations

What is the explanation for a situation where a person hears voices which order them around? How can we explain the situation of a young woman who refuses to eat because she is afraid of being poisoned? How is it possible for a man to become violent, just because his father asked how he is getting on? What causes a grown man to stop washing himself, never change his clothes and sleep every day until noon?

We have seen that science assumes that schizophrenia is basically a disturbance in the biochemistry of the brain.[11] In chapter 3, I proposed a model of the brain as a computer. In so doing I was careful to make sure that this way of looking at it did not exclude pastoral concerns, but rather extended them, and particularly where schizophrenia is concerned, led to a better understanding of the illness.

Let us briefly recall what is involved in the information processing in the human brain. First of all comes perception. We continually receive impressions through our sense organs (ears, eyes, etc.). In the brain's control centre this information is interpreted, sorted, and stored. We call this process thought. In connection with this we distinguish between the content of thought, and thinking as a process. The sentences you are reading here are part of the 'content' of this book. However, what you do with them, how you take up the information and hold it in your memory, would come under the heading of the thinking process.

Now let us turn to our schizophrenic patients whose control centres so to speak have been disturbed. Their thought process is no longer capable of correctly interpreting, valuing, sorting and storing the information which keeps pouring in. Perceptions are distorted and linked with inappropriate feelings from the memory—hallucinations are the result. The contents of the memory are called back to the conscious mind (on to the projector screen) without the voluntary command of the control centre, and then combined with other things. For example the sick person may suddenly hear his own thoughts, but in the tones of his sister's voice.

Experiences and ideas, fears and desires, are called out of the memory store without obvious reason and thrown together as if in a gigantic jigsaw puzzle. For near relatives the individual ideas and words still, more or less, make sense. They know the experiences of their sick relative and can still draw together threads from the bizarre comments—but the outsider is a stranger in this world. During a schizophrenic attack, the divisions between real experiences and the inner world become permeable. Fantasy and reality are melted together into a chaotic system of delusion. The afflicted person tries in vain to drag his surroundings out of the deceptive world of his madness and into reality, but again and again waves of psychosis break over him. It is no wonder that this also leads to reactions in the patient which can be difficult to understand. He is no longer in a position to apply his faculties and his behaviour to a concrete situation. Once I waved to a patient in a friendly way. But he ducked as if I had thrown a stone at him. He had noticed my movement, but interpreted it wrongly, and linked it with feelings of fear and threat. For him, his reaction was logical, but from my point of view it was bizarre.

So now we understand better how schizophrenic symptoms come into being. But in Christian circles there are further questions to ask: What is the explanation of religious mania? How should schizophrenic symptoms be categorised from a spiritual perspective? I will deal with these questions in the next chapter.

CHAPTER TEN

SCHIZOPHRENIA AND FAITH

'*D*octor, I'm in terrible trouble' an elderly lady complained to me. 'Tonight I should have gone to Heaven, but my room-mate stopped me. God allowed her to torment me, and now I can't forgive her any more. Do you know, two years ago, I committed a terrible sin. The doctor wanted to take my blood, but I wouldn't let him. I didn't realise at the time that I should have made a great sacrifice. It's because I didn't give my blood that God hasn't taken me to be with him yet.'

What sense would you make of a story like that? How would you advise the woman? Would you teach her about the once-for-all true sacrifice that opens the way to God? Would you encourage her to forgive? Or try to help her see that she was imagining it all?

These are the kind of questions which will face a pastoral counsellor who is dealing with schizophrenic people during a delusive phase. It is not uncommon to meet sick people who use a Christian vocabulary and thus have what in the broadest sense of the word could be termed as 'religious mania'. This observation throws up a host of questions for christians as well as non-believers. Often, false conclusions are drawn from the use of religious terms. Even among doctors and other members of the caring professions one hears over and over again the widespread opinion that a person's psychosis has been caused by religious involvement. At very least, the impression is given that 'religious mania' is a negative outcome of the existence of religion in society.

These assertions are based on prejudice, rather than on careful scientific research. I will look into a few studies on the theme of religious mania in a later section, but first of all I will explain how 'religious mania' comes about, and how it can be understood.

Explaining Religious Delusions

Basically, three forms of religious delusion can be distinguished:

a) Religious images used to explain schizophrenic experiences
b) Delusive distortions of genuine religious faith
c) Mistaken interpretation of religious terms and unusual beliefs on the part of the counsellor.

The first two are to be regarded as characteristic ways in which schizophrenic people make sense of their experience. The third form of religious delusion derives from the prejudice and lack of understanding of a counsellor who is faced with expressions of religious faith with which he is not familiar.

a) RELIGIOUS IMAGES USED TO EXPLAIN SCHIZO-PHRENIC EXPERIENCE. To those affected by them, the experiences involved in a schizophrenic mental disorder seem very eerie, 'supernatural', strange and menacing. They are plagued by ideas and fears which they cannot explain in terms of their previous frames of reference. They feel as if they have abilities and a calling which is more than normal, yet they also notice the destructive influence of the illness on their work, their relationships and eventually, their own personality.

How can a person like this make sense of the experiences which break over him during a psychosis? Often earthbound images are no longer sufficient for this task. However, in religious teaching he has heard about angels and demons, prophetic messages and signs and wonders. In this way even people who are not normally influenced by Christian faith develop the most fantastic religious delusions. When the schizophrenic attack subsides, their faith also returns to its previous level.

b) DELUSIVE DISTORTIONS OF GENUINE RELIGIOUS FAITH. The patient has a healthy faith before his or her illness. Nevertheless like other aspects of life, this comes to be experienced and expressed in a distorted way. I am reminded of a young woman, a believer, who suddenly felt a need to be 'on fire for the Lord', in contrast to her earlier behaviour. She became motivated more and more by thoughts about 'the lost'. She reached a point where she could hardly sleep, and she gave out piles of tracts. One day, out of the blue she injured her wrist with a knife. She explained to her shocked parents that she had shed her blood for the lost because it was Good Friday. With treatment, the disturbance subsided in the course of a few days, and her spiritual life suffered no harm as a result. Today the young woman is married and an active member of her church.

Depressive delusions, which can take on grotesque forms, such as thoughts of having committed terrible sins, also belong to this category. In this connection, please refer to the chapter on 'Depression' (PAGE 99).

c) UNUSUAL EXPRESSIONS OF FAITH are sometimes misunderstood by carers as an expression of the illness in schizophrenic patients, in spite of the fact that thesemay express the actual beliefs and practices of his church or religious group. At this point a great deal of understanding of unusual forms of Christian thought is necessary to avoid doing the patient an injustice. If a Bible College student expresses the desire to 'tell everyone about Jesus', it doesn't necessarily mean he is suffering from a 'missionary mania', even if he is also suffering from a schizophrenic disorder. He has simply been trained to pass on the gospel to other people, just as the Bible teaches.

It becomes more difficult, when a German lady explains that she has been 'delivered from a Hitler demon'. In order to be able to decide whether this is a delusion or just a strange teaching, you need to know that this was said by a certain 'pastoral counsellor' who in a routine way persuaded many other mentally healthy fellow believers of German origin that in order to grow spiritually they needed deliverance from a 'Hitler spirit'. (This happened in Switzerland in 1985).

Granted, circumstances like this strain the understanding of the most tolerant psychiatrist, and they make it easier to understand why people who work in the field of psychiatry are often prejudiced against believers. It is especially important here to distinguish between belief, superstition and delusion.[1] Nevertheless, a Christian has the right to be taken just as seriously in a psychiatric hospital as an environmental campaigner, or a psychotic 'peace-freak', whose opinions may be closer to those of the staff.

Does Christianity Make You Ill?

This question can be answered by a clear 'no', since two research projects in Swiss psychiatric hospitals have demonstrated that no connection can be established between religious upbringing and religious mania.[2] One author comes to the conclusion: 'In this way the surprising result of our study indicates that a strong religious interest in the parental home is more often linked with a weak religious element in the psychotic theme than with a strong one.'[3]

Generally it is true to say that religious delusion is only one of several themes of insanity. *One should never conclude from the content of the delusion that the cause of the schizophrenic illness is to be found within it.* This would be just as absurd as holding technology responsible for the onset of a schizophrenia in which the patient felt himself influenced by lasers and computers, or blaming environmentalists for the development of a 'green mania'.

What *does* influence the theme of delusions? Much evidence points to the probability that the dominant ideas and world view of a culture in turn influence the content of the delusions which occur. Kranz, the German psychiatrist, researched the contents of patients' delusions in 1886, 1916, and 1946, and could demonstrate how the discovery of new technologies (e.g. radio) or equally the rise of the Fuhrer, coloured the delusive ideas of the mentally ill.[4] More recent studies have established that over the decade a change has taken place in the frequency of particular themes of delusion.[5]

Delusive ideas are often formed by the experiences and activities which for the patient are bound up with strong feelings (fear, love, failure or rejection). In our age, where life is no longer shaped so much by faith in God, we also find fewer religious delusions. In contrast, in recent years, against a background of dying forests, chemical accidents and nuclear catastrophes, a delusive environmental fear has clearly taken hold.

To sum up, it can be said that a delusion may have a religious slant to it, but no conclusion can be drawn from this about the cause of the illness. The development of a delusion can be better understood by reference to a sick person's life situation and personality structure, but never completely explained by it.

Schizophrenia in the Literature of Pastoral Care

Having offered some explanations of schizophrenic symptoms from a scientific viewpoint, I would like to briefly examine one or two theories found in Christian books. Anyone who thumbs through the available literature on the subject of pastoral care will find three main approaches:

a) Recognition of schizophrenia as a sickness, with no particular pastoral point of view.

b) Emphasising sin and irresponsibility.
c) Emphasising a demonic cause ('occult bondage').

It is necessary for me to comment briefly on these models, in order to shed light on an area which causes many Christians insecurity, and extra difficulty with their sick relatives. From what I have said already it will be clear that schizophrenia is to be viewed as an illness which requires medical treatment. However, establishing that schizophrenia is an illness does not exclude the need for pastoral care. Concepts must therefore be developed which enable us to counsel and care for the needs of fellow christians with schizophrenia.

Schizophrenia and Sin

Jay Adam's school of pastoral counselling emphasised the role of sin and personal responsibility. Psychosis was seen as an avoidance of confrontation with biblical truths and a flight from responsible living. For instance, if a young man became psychotic after a failure at school, this was seen as a way to avoid facing the fact of his failure and the responsibility of disciplined work.[6]

I would not wish to question Adam's basic intention to bring biblical truth back into pastoral care. Unfortunately his writings show an outdated and one-sided reading of the nature of schizophrenia, even at the points where he still admits the possibility of an 'organic' cause. Although the sinfulness of human beings is the cause of many difficulties, this concept cannot be applied in a short-circuiting way to schizophrenia.

It can be very misleading to link two statements with the word 'because'. Consider the following sentence: 'Car accidents occur because cars pollute the atmosphere.' Both statements are absolutely true, but the link made between them isn't. All cars pollute the atmosphere, but in only a tiny percentage of cases does the pollution become the cause of an accident. In addition to this, we know that there are many other contributory causes for accidents, besides pollution of the atmosphere. Now consider the following fact: All human

beings sin, but only one per cent become ill with
schizophrenia. Are we then to blame the afflicted person's sin
for his illness, without looking for other causes?

Schizophrenic people are capable of sin, as we all are. It
may seem banal, but they can also be forgiven, as we all can.
In less severe situations in particular, schizophrenic people
enter an in-between phase where they can be accountable in a
normal way. In chronic cases, much of the patient's
behaviour is affected by the sickness and not caused by any
evil intent. So I have to ask: 'Is it sin, if a chronic
schizophrenic continues, even after many warnings, to clomp
around at night in clogs and never wash himself? In my
opinion, no, although I agree that such behaviour is disturbing
. . . perhaps so much so that it would no longer be possible to
keep the patient at home because those who live with him can
no longer cope with his unrest.

Schizophrenia and the Occult

A few writers of books on pastoral care suggest a causal
connection between schizophrenia and demonic influence.
The following quotations are all taken from the same book .[7]

First the author asserts 'all the descriptions of psychosis
which we find in the Bible show the characteristics of guilt
and occult bondage.' From this basis he argues that all
psychoses in our time are connected in the same ways. To the
question, 'why are more Christians not aware of this?' he
replies, 'so the chief reason for this mistaken understanding of
the psychoses would seem to lie in the fact that the
sensitisation of the spirit, which is needed for the demonic
powers to manifest and become active, was clearly never, or
only seldom successful.'

There are still more problems of explanation. How can a
person who has never allowed themselves to become involved
in occult practices still become prey to a psychotic condition?
The answer: 'the occult problem of a psychotic person never
has its beginning in his own lifetime. I was always able to

trace a line of demonic oppression back for at least two and usually three to four generations.'

This has consequences for treatment. Deliverance ministry will be necessary, but unfortunately, usually unsuccessful. The explanation: 'Deliverance ministry to a psychotic Christian is tiring, and usually time-consuming . . . if the foundation of faith needed for active progress in loosing and deliverance has not been laid in the pastoral counsellors and the church which accepts responsibility for the patient, it is better to hand the sick person to the hospital for the time being for psychopharmaceutical treatment. The time for a spiritual offensive will come later.'

So now the church is to blame for the fact that the psychotic person hasn't improved. The patient is finally shoved into the hospital where 'worldly' people can look after him until he has recovered enough for the pastoral counsellor who specialises in occult situations to blast him with the next spiritual offensive. I would like to leave the reader to judge whether such an approach is helpful, compassionate, or even biblical.

So does occult activity not play any role in schizophrenic people? Here the same applies as with the question of sin and schizophrenia. Schizophrenia can also be mixed up with occult involvement. But confession and deliverance ministry do not bring release of the whole problem. It is a great injustice therefore to believers who are experiencing a psychotic crisis, to brand them as 'demonised' and subject them to stressful exorcism rituals.

Exorcisms in this situation often lead to a worsening of the psychosis as Dr. Margies indirectly admits himself: 'The person who exceeds his faith will experience bitter disappointment'.[8]

So far I have not been able to recognise any improvement in the external situation and spiritual life, let alone the basic illness of patients, resulting from models of pastoral care which point back in a one-sided way to sin or occult bondage. Much more frequently the relatives' and patients' trust in the pastoral counsellor is destroyed to such an extent that any co-operation between the doctor and the pastoral counsellor is rendered impossible.

So, how can we deal with schizophrenic people in a pastoral context? Are there alternative approaches? Can psychiatric and pastoral help be integrated? What possibilities lie open for biblical pastoral care of schizophrenic people? These are the questions we shall address in the next chapter.

CHAPTER ELEVEN

SCHIZOPHRENIA: THERAPY AND PASTORAL CARE

*T*he treatment of schizophrenia has changed dramatically in the last thirty years. When I look through the case notes of my patients I am always moved by the terrible impasse in which schizophrenic people found themselves prior to 1950. There was hardly any way to ease their restless anxiety and delusive ideas. Doctors and other medical staff grasped at doubtful straws in the attempt to make life more bearable for these sick people who frequently would become so absorbed in their psychotic inner world, that conversation from outside no longer reached them. The thought of a return to their family was out of the question.

Even mild schizophrenic attacks which nowadays subside in a matter of weeks used to last months or years without medication. Hannah Green gives a striking picture of this period in her book 'I never promised you a rose garden.'[1] Today the time when patients were calmed down by being wrapped in wet sheets or sat in covered hip-baths is long since past.

Nowadays most schizophrenic people live outside the hospital. Their care is the responsibility not only of doctors and caring professionals, but of pastoral counsellors and the relatives who live with them. In the following pages I will show some possible approaches to the care of schizophrenic people, which take account of medical and social as well as pastoral aspects. The best possible care can only be achieved when all those involved work together.

Three Supporting Pillars in the Treatment of Schizophrenia

The multitude of different approaches to the treatment of schizophrenia can be divided into three main groups:

1. Medication (with neuroleptic drugs)
2. An ordered daily routine
3. An emotional climate conducive to improvement.

1.   Medication Since disturbances in the biochemistry of the brain play an important role in schizophrenia, medication has a fundamental influence on the condition. Neuroleptic drugs are the medication of choice (such as Halidol, Clopixol, or Clozaril, to name a few). They generally lead to a calming and ordering of the thought processes. Continued medication under the supervision of a doctor is the most important pillar in the prevention of a relapse.

Unfortunately, not all problems can be solved even by this kind of regular intake of medication. To be honest, severe and insidious forms of schizophrenia are only affected to an unsatisfactory extent. Nevertheless, if the schizophrenic patient is only rendered a little calmer, it can make it easier for relatives to take care of him at home, instead of having to hand him over to the hospital.

Neuroleptic drugs, like all others, have side effects. Muscle cramps, drowsiness, excessive salivation, and restlessness in the legs are the most common. However, these can be controlled by additional medication in the majority of cases. As a general rule of thumb, the drugs are given in the correct dosage if the acute symptoms are under control and normal sleep patterns are maintained.

2.   Daily Routine Schizophrenic people frequently find it difficult to order their day. For this reason, modern psychiatric practice will be to encourage a programme of occupational therapy during the week, whether within the hospital or outside in a sheltered workshop. They need protection from stress on the one hand, but training for their remaining abilities as well as contact with other people on the other. A regular daily routine is important for the following reasons:

a) A clear timetabled programme helps the patient to be orientated and breaks up the monotony of a long day.

b) It communicates to the patient the sense that he is needed and can do something useful.

c) It provides a break for relatives and spreads the burden of care so that it rests on more shoulders.

3. *Emotional Climate* People who suffer from schizophrenia are generally less able than others to cope with pressure. The adjustment of their environment, especially that of their relatives, can contribute to the prevention of a relapse. It is necessary to accept the patient with his limitations, without taking all responsibility away from him.

That is not always easy. A few years ago now, researchers thought they had established that the reaction of relatives was an important factor in dispersing the illness. 'E.E.-research' (expressed emotions) confirmed that the relatives of patients who made a good recovery accepted them better, criticised them less and gave them more independence. The conclusion was drawn from this observation that patients recovered well because their relatives behaved in this way. However, it is becoming increasingly clear today that the opposite was the case. The relatives found it easier to behave in this way because the patient was improving so well.[2] Nevertheless the relatives and carers need continual encouragement to show the sick person love in the right way, and to set boundaries for him.

A Word about the Psychotherapy of Schizophrenia

In support of the three pillars mentioned above, supportive conversations and sympathetic advice can be very valuable for the patient. Particularly in times of crisis, they are grateful for the support of a professional person outside the situation who can help them overcome the problems they face.

However, psychotherapy in the strict sense has not proved valuable with schizophrenic patients.[3] For most schizophrenic people psychotherapy is an excessive burden, indeed it can cause a great deal of damage. Attempts to release feelings and work through hidden motives are particularly dangerous. I have observed several relapses and even suicides which have been triggered by psychodynamic group therapies, transactional analysis, primal scream therapy and similar approaches.

At this point it needs to be said that intensive approaches to pastoral care can have the same results.[4] Treatment of schizophrenia belongs properly in the hands of the doctor, supported by sympathetic carers, pastoral counsellors included, who know their limitations. We now need to consider what contribution can be made to the therapy of schizophrenic people by biblically orientated pastoral care.

Pastoral Care for the Schizophrenic Person

Counselling depends on the ability of a person to take part in a conversation, on his ability to understand, properly interpret and apply the things that are said. However, when it comes to people suffering from schizophrenia...particularly during an active phase . . . the severe disturbance to their thought processes which results from the illness means that there are severe limits to what can be achieved through counselling sessions.

The conversational ability of schizophrenic people can be differentiated in accordance with the various phases through which the illness passes. A patient is least capable of receiving benefit from counselling during an acute psychotic phase. In between times normal conversation is often possible. The same applies to the spiritual life. This is severely disrupted by the disturbed thought processes but can nevertheless become completely normal again, and when it returns can be an important support for the patient.

In view of this I would like to deal with the possibilities and limitations in the pastoral care of schizophrenic people in two sections, namely i) in the acute phase and ii) during the residual phase (including the residual intermediate phase).

How to Respond to Acute Symptoms[5]

1. Keep calm and try to keep bringing the person back all the time to the level of reality, in other words, talk to them about the real situation, even when they find it hard to receive what you are saying. The circumstances under which admission to a hospital becomes necessary, can be very dramatic. As a result the pastoral helper can easily get left out of the picture at this point.

2. Be logical and do everything to motivate the sick person to receive medical treatment. These sick people basically need to be cared for by a medical specialist. Only rarely can someone with an acute attack of schizophrenia be successfully treated as an outpatient. As a rule these people have no insight into their illness. For this reason in certain circumstances it is necessary for this decision to be taken out of the hands of the sick person. If you have to do this you should not show any sign of personal uncertainty. Since these patients have been disorientated, as counsellors we have to give them clear direction.

3. Behave in a natural and unpressured way. Don't put on a kind of protective patronising manner, but behave in a friendly way to the sick person, talking quite naturally with them.

4. Visit the sick person during his stay in hospital so

that he doesn't lose contact with the normal world. It is important, in this connection, that during his hospital stay the sick person is prepared for what will be waiting for him afterwards. It will be important both during the stay in hospital, and even more so afterwards, to talk in an encouraging way about God's love and the love of the people at church, and to stress God's ability to carry him through.

One word of caution is needed, however: Visits should be arranged, to begin with, in careful consultation with the medical staff. For a sick person whose nerves have been weakened, visits can be very stressful and lead to a further worsening of his condition.

Pastoral Care on the Return From Hospital

Medical treatment does not put careful pastoral support right out of the picture. On the contrary, the very thing a believer needs when he or she has gone through the distressing experience of a psychosis, is to understand and work through the illness in the light of their faith. What questions will they be likely to bring to the pastoral counsellor? In the consultations I have had, the questions I have encountered fall into three groups:

1. Questions of meaning and faith
2. Questions about the illness: it's causes, prognosis, medication, etc.
3. Questions about coping with life:
   a) Coping with reduced ability to endure stress
   b) Practical arrangements for living
   c) Advice and comfort for relatives

Questions of Meaning and Faith

The experience of a psychosis raises questions for the believing patient and his relatives, which they are not usually able to voice to the psychiatrist. Here are a few examples:

- Why has God let this happen?
- Where does the illness come from? Does sin or occult bondage lie at the back of it?
- We have tried everything. Why isn't prayer working?
- Why is his spiritual life so disturbed?
- (From Dora, a 23-year-old saleswoman) 'I don't have any assurance of faith any more! It seems as if my neighbour has stolen it. She's always looking at me with a dark expression on her face.'
- (Reinhard, 32, a teacher) 'I'm often so tired that I can't make sense of the Bible any more. I just lie around all the time. Can God really still help me?
- and finally: 'Is there still hope?'

You will notice that there is no simple answer to any of these questions. We often have to struggle with the suffering of the schizophrenic patient in much the same way as with that of the cancer victim. In this phase pastoral care needs to be characterised by compassion and patience. Not in a resigned kind of waiting, but actively 'helping the weak' in the knowledge and certainty of God's Word. Christians have a hope which reaches beyond such things as health, the ability to work, or riches and happiness!

There is no need to pay too much attention to religious delusions, because in most cases they will die away of their own accord. The best thing you can do is to hold the patient to the Biblical facts in simple words, full of conviction. For example, you could respond to Dora's question in this way: 'Maybe sometimes you're not able to hold on to your faith the way you used to. But Jesus is faithful. He is stronger than all the powers of darkness. He holds us even when we don't have the strength to hold on to Him any more. You will get your joy back again. It just needs time for you to get better again.'

Reinhard's case involves a man who used to be a teacher, who has already been unfit for work for eight years (residual state). He needs continual reassurance that his value to God does not depend on his career. For him the promise is especially relevant which says 'The Spirit of God comes to our aid. We are weak and do not know how we should pray. For this reason the Spirit approaches God on our behalf with groans which cannot be expressed in words'.[6]

The answers in these situations are similar to those in the care of people who suffer from severe physical disabilities. I have continually experienced how patients in the weakness of a residual schizophrenic state learn to trust God and draw strength from His Word. Of course, it goes without saying that pastoral counselling should not stand in isolation from practical support and advice for the patient and his relatives.

Questions About The Illness

Precisely because schizophrenia is so difficult to understand, the pastoral counsellor, no less than medical personnel, will be confronted with questions about the illness, and will need to be in a position to give some answers. If you have read this book carefully, you will be able to answer the most important questions about the causes, understanding, and course of schizophrenia.

Often the sufferer will also want to hear what the pastoral counsellor thinks about the medication. 'Do I still have to take tablets? 'they may ask, 'I don't want to become an addict!' Under no circumstances should someone seeking advice be encouraged to stop taking neuroleptic drugs. Always direct them towards their doctor and explain to them how helpful medication can be, even when it means putting up with a few side-effects. It is better to be able to live, work and attend church outside the hospital, than to slip into a psychosis without tablets or injections. Regular use of neuroleptic drugs should not be compared with an addiction. A better comparison is with the regular administration of insulin to a diabetic, who also suffers, of course, from a disturbance of the body's metabolism. As a general rule, the ability to regularly get sufficient sleep is a good sign that the time may be right for a reduction of the medication. If you notice that a schizophrenic person is suddenly sleeping less and is more strongly driven, get in touch with his doctor.

Compassion and Patience

Relatives often need to talk as well. How often they find themselves in the dilemma of asking 'To what extent is the patient's behaviour caused by the illness, and to what extent is it intentional? How should we respond? And at what point does it become necessary to admit the afflicted person to hospital again?' Even experts are not always able to answer these questions. Often it is not, in the first instance, a matter of right and wrong, but more a question of how much the carers can cope with in a particular situation. Pastoral counsellors who care for schizophrenic people need a great deal of patience and a willingness to carry the burdens of sick people and their families, without seeing spectacular changes. Nevertheless, this does not imply that there is any reason to lose hope. Do not forget that, with correct treatment, 75 per cent of all cases improve, though it takes considerable time. Those who share these burdens should be encouraged by the promise, 'so will you fulfil the law of Christ!'.[7] It isn't enough to give them admonitions from the Bible. If you really want to help people who have a chronic psychiatric illness, you will need to discover afresh the meaning of comforting and supportive pastoral care.

Rehabilitation: An Encouragement or an Excessive Demand?

Often well-meaning pastoral counsellors (not to mention behaviourally-orientated social workers and psychologists) tend to overstretch the patient and his family. I once asked a doctor who was a committed Christian, 'What is your goal in the treatment of schizophrenic patients?' I was dismayed by his answer: 'For them to be as healthy as I am!'

Why was I dismayed? Is this request unreasonable? Certainly, the wish is good, but the effect of it can be that you expect too much from the patient, and hence from yourself. In the long term, the result is always disappointment, for the patient as much as the helper.

Schizophrenic patients who already have several attacks behind them and show an obvious reduction in their general performance are less capable of handling pressure, even in their 'good' times. The personality of a chronic schizophrenic patient is sometimes described as 'silted up'. That is a good way to describe these emotionally flattened people who are incapable of handling pressure and have little self-initiative. Such people can be activated to a pronounced degree through the kind of committed care that can be provided in residential homes and communities. Nevertheless, it is essential to recognise the boundary between encouragement, and making excessive demands. It is certainly possible to train these patients to a certain degree and spur them on to a higher performance, but in the process they are often placed under an uncomfortable pressure to succeed, a tension which can lead to a further relapse. Without constant supervision they do not have the power within them to apply independently what they have learned before. They are like crumbling sandstone, which cannot be returned to its former shape.

Therapists who do not recognise these boundaries remind me of children who apply themselves to build a sandcastle with enthusiasm and effort, but almost as soon as their work is left to the wind and the waves the signs of decay begin to show . . . the beautiful towers and carefully excavated gateways are washed away.

This is why we need to ask 'Where are the limits of what can be attained by our chronically ill patients? And which is of more value: A person who lives within their limits and is content with them, or a chronically overtaxed patient who can only maintain his level through the constant efforts of a number of carers? If attempts at rehabilitation have shown that a patient is pushing his limitations, we have to accept these and help him to make the best of them. It can no longer be the carer's job to groom him to be a star performer in a competitive society. We are not called to build impressive sandcastles, but to lovingly create a context in which the fragile sandstructures of the chronic schizophrenic person can survive. To protect him, care for him and carry him, in the full knowledge of his weakness.

PART III

HELPING THE WEAK

CHAPTER TWELVE

INTEGRATED CARE OF THE MENTALLY ILL

*H*ow can we best help someone who is going through a psychiatric crisis? Is there an integrated view of the treatment of people suffering with mental illness which offers help without resigning itself to their condition, and awakens hope without churning out empty platitudes? Furthermore, can any basis for a comprehensive overview of the practical pastoral care of the mentally ill be derived from the Bible?

Multidimensional Perspective

In the course of this book one thing has become clear: Psychiatric disorders are not to be understood with the use of simple models. Our knowledge of the causes and treatment is, like so many things, in part. The Bible points us in the right direction, but doesn't contain answers to every question of detail in psychiatry, just as it does not tell us how to perform an appendicectomy.

The complicated interactions can only be described for the most part by models which are incapable of giving us a complete picture. The contour lines on a map can never convey the experience of a traveller on seeing the Matterhorn. In the same way the most detailed knowledge about the nature of psychiatric illnesses, even together with the most fascinating theories about the best way of giving care cannot convey the personal struggle experienced by the counsellor who takes on the care of a mentally ill person. For this reason

I do not intend to go into details about the great schools of psychiatric thought which have developed in the course of the years.

They have all described aspects of human existence, but all too often they get stuck at one level. While some stress working through childhood experiences, others restrict themselves to therapy by medication. One will put the patient's own experience at the centre, others plead for a systemic change in the family as the basis for healing. Similar developments can be seen in the field of pastoral care. Here we find a broad spectrum stretching from rules for behaviour based on Biblical texts at one end, to inner healing through spiritually induced experiences at the other.

Anyone who views a person solely in one dimension whether at the physical level (disposition) in social relationships (environment) or at the level of his own thought and behaviour (reaction) will leave out important aspects. Indeed, I doubt if that approach will really be of any help at all. Our goal, in our search for understanding, must therefore be to develop a *multidimensional perspective*,[1] which keeps the most diverse points of view under consideration, and makes an effort to see the human being as a whole.

The Goal of Pastoral Care

What is the proper goal for the pastoral care of the mentally ill? Often people give the spontaneous answer: 'to make them well again!' In fact, many people who go through mental illness do have a good chance of being completely restored. However, others suffer throughout their lives from the limitations imposed by psychiatric illness. They are not best served by one-sided catchphrases such as 'wholeness' and 'spiritual health'. For them, the goal has to be redefined. Help for those who are psychiatrically weak doesn't consist in re-establishing the situation as it was before the illness occurred, or in adapting to the ideals of our competitive society. It is advisable not to just direct one's gaze in a one-sided way to the symptoms or course of the illness and try to remove them. In the case of severe disorders of a person's thought world (depressive withdrawal, compulsive rituals or paranoid delusions, for example) that is often simply not possible.

The therapeutic goal of effective long-term care must be directed towards *coping with existence* in this world with all its limitations. This approach, combining compassion and reality, is Christian at the deepest level and goes far beyond treating sick people in a resigned way because 'they can't be helped'.[2]

Biblical Pastoral Care is Practical

In the first chapter I defined pastoral care briefly as help to cope with life based on a foundation of biblical principles. This implies that pastoral care and counselling go far beyond a mundane concept involving discussions of matters of faith. Pastoral counselling, as I find it in the Bible, does not, in the first instance, try to explain the causes of events, but helps us to understand their purpose, and to direct our life to achieving a new goal. For this reason, I regard with concern tendencies in the field of pastoral counselling which attempt to establish supposed causes of a disorder, and in the process neglect compassionate empathy with the patient's suffering.

The Bible reflects a whole spectrum of helpful approaches which can assist a sick person, and a mentally ill person in particular, in coping with life. Paul warns the early Christians to develop a wide-ranging programme of pastoral care.[3]

- admonish the idle
- encourage the fainthearted
- help the weak
- be patient with everyone.

What do these four statements imply for contact with the mentally ill? *First*: The carer should be in a position to correctly distinguish between different situations (differential diagnosis). He should be able to distinguish between 'idle, fainthearted and weak'.

'Idle' people are those who, all things considered, are capable of coping with life, but are living sinfully and behaving in such a way as to bring problems on themselves. They need to be warned and pointed in the right direction. By 'faint-hearted', I understand those people who are unquestionably going through a crisis made up of difficult life situations and inner conflicts. They often suffer from feelings of rejection and low self esteem, inhibitions and anxieties which cast a shadow over their spiritual life as well.

And the 'weak' are people whose existence is plainly restricted as a result of physical and psychological handicaps. With the best will in the world they are no longer able to carry a full load, whether in everyday life, or in their Christian duties. Nevertheless, they are of no less value in God's eyes. They need a special measure of compassionate acceptance on the part of their fellows.

Secondly: different problems should be treated in different ways (differential therapy). All too often truths which are certainly helpful in moderate cases are applied without question to people who are suffering from severe mental illness, for whom these principles are no longer valid. Depressed people are so often unjustly treated by people who take their exaggerated guilt feelings as a cue to make them confess and repent, even though they have already pleaded for forgiveness many times for each and every tiny little sin. Evangelical pastoral counsellors in particular, are in danger of emphasising only the corrective kind of pastoral care. But when you are dealing with people who are suffering from a mental illness, it is more appropriate to draw attention back to the *comforting* words of the Holy Scripture and be prepared to *help* the weak person in the practical concerns of everyday life.

Thirdly: wounds of the soul take time to heal. With good reason Paul admonishes the Christians in Thessalonica 'Have

patience with everyone!' Patience is not passive, but active.
It doesn't signify resigned submission to the adversities of
life, but 'that action which opens itself to one's neighbour,
meets him, and opens up the opportunity of a common life.
Human patience and long-suffering in this sense is thus not a
quality of character, but rather an act, indeed the first act, of
love'.[4]

Figure 12-1

A Comprehensive Model of helping

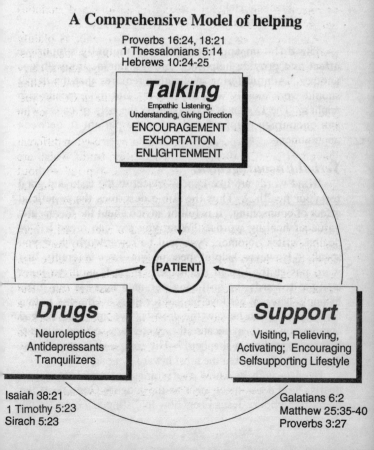

Proverbs 16:24, 18:21
1 Thessalonians 5:14
Hebrews 10:24-25

Talking
Empathic Listening,
Understanding, Giving Direction
ENCOURAGEMENT
EXHORTATION
ENLIGHTENMENT

PATIENT

Drugs
Neuroleptics
Antidepressants
Tranquilizers

Isaiah 38:21
1 Timothy 5:23
Sirach 5:23

Support
Visiting, Relieving,
Activating; Encouraging
Selfsupporting Lifestyle

Galatians 6:2
Matthew 25:35-40
Proverbs 3:27

In the diagram above I have tried to present a simple model of the comprehensive help needed by those who are mentally ill. In the centre stands the patient with his internal conflicts and external problems. Depending on the nature of his basic problem he will need the opportunity to receive one or more of several kinds of help. These I have summed up in three groups:

1. Counselling
2. Practical Help
3. Medication

The different approaches have a mutually supportive effect and provide help only through interacting with one another. Administering medication requires that the helper should work closely with the doctor. But the opposite also applies. The Doctor is dependent on the help of carers who can encourage, support and carry the patient in between appointments.

Verbal Encouragement

'Kind words are like honey—sweet to the taste and good for your health'.[5] Thus the Bible describes the beneficial effect of counselling. It is full of advice about the therapeutic value of healing words. 'What you say can mean life or death,' writes Solomon, 'you will be rewarded by how you speak.'[6] However, helpful speech begins even before the first word passes the lips of the helper. It starts with our inner attitude towards the suffering person. Jesus is our great example here. What love he had for those who came to him for help! 'When he saw the crowds,' we are told, 'he had compassion on them because they were harassed and helpless, like sheep without a shepherd'[7] His compassion was not just demeaning charity, but the most inward sympathy.[8]

Even though he knew everything that was in people's hearts, he did not meet them as the judging God but as the merciful Saviour. Jesus knew how to distinguish between the strong and the weak. He could use strong words to correct the pharisees, with their arrogant dogmatism, but he met the weak with compassion and love.[9]

This attitude of compassion towards the weak which I have sketched out in this book is the most important pre-requisite for comforting and supportive conversation with mentally ill people. In addition, a further condition is needed: *willingness to listen*. Listening means paying attention to the other person without beginning to think over what you are going to say when they have finished, while they are still talking. James warns his readers: 'Everyone should be quick to listen, slow to speak, and slow to become angry'.[10] What starts as silent attention can during the course of an interview move into *active listening*.[11] By this I mean asking gentle clarifying questions, which encourage the counsellee to come out of himself and open his heart.

In this connection it is always advisable to resist the inward compulsion to be too quick to give explanations and advice. A great deal of empathetic skill and patience is needed to strike the right note. Psychiatrically weaker people are often enormously sensitive. For this reason the pastoral counsellor must take careful note of the personality and situation of the person he is dealing with. He must be continually asking himself 'which words could trigger a reaction in this person?' and 'how can I help this person to grow inwardly and cope better with life?' Finally, the pastoral counsellor needs to know his *limitations*. When you are talking to mentally ill people you cannot always set the same goals as in conversation with people who are receptive to a normal degree. The more severe the suffering and more acute the situation, the more restricted the patient's conversational ability will be. This connection is represented diagrammatically in Figure 12-2.

As became clear when I was describing the various separate illnesses, patients in severe depression and acute schizophrenic crises are scarcely receptive to their environment. It would be illusory to try to share biblical truths with them in an orderly way at this time of inner confusion and doubt. What is needed at this point is healthy intelligence without unworldly dogmatism, a practical and resolute approach which does not shrink from co-operation with the doctor, nor from the use of medication.

Figure 12-2

Conversational Ability and Severity of an Illness

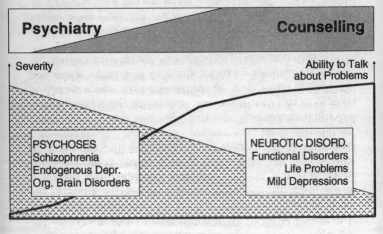

Psychiatry   Counselling

↑ Severity   Ability to Talk
                                        about Problems

PSYCHOSES
Schizophrenia
Endogenous Depr.
Org. Brain Disorders

NEUROTIC DISORD.
Functional Disorders
Life Problems
Mild Depressions

Of course, pastoral care isn't dependent on the spoken word alone. The Christian, more than anyone, knows that his own efforts can do nothing unless God himself is at work in the patient. Jesus undergirded his words and his actions with his prayers. In intercession the pastoral counsellor enters a new level of effectiveness, even when he can do nothing for the patient outwardly.

Praying Together with the Patient   This often helps more than any number of words and quotations from the Bible. A lady with a severe depression recounted to me how she had been to see her pastor and shared her difficulties with him. She could scarcely take in the things he said, but then he anointed her with oil and prayed over her together with one of the elders of the church. This act of loving attention and blessing did her an immeasurable amount of good, and gave her new courage to go on living.

In this connection many pastoral counsellors would point us in the direction of *deliverance from occult powers*, regarding this as of special importance with mentally ill people. They call into play texts in the gospels where Jesus drove demons out of people whose behaviour was odd. However, experience shows that it is very difficult to transfer these situations and apply them to someone with an endogenous psychosis. For this reason the utmost restraint is advised in too quickly assuming a demonic cause for psychiatric disorders.[12] Many patients with minor disorders have been greatly helped by deliverance ministry from a pastoral counsellor, but with many others it has had exactly the opposite effect. Instead of experiencing inner freedom, they have found their psychiatric problems have become worse, because instead of concentrating their attention on God's ability to support them and help them through, they have slipped into an anxious fixation on the demonic powers. Dr. Lechler, a well-known Christian psychiatrist once wrote: 'I have lost count of the cases in which I have observed the unhealthy effect on a mentally ill person of falsely labelling them as demonised. It is a great injustice for someone who is suffering emotionally and spiritually in this way to be told that he or she is in the Devil's power. Anyone who makes such an accusation without any knowledge of the workings of a sick soul, or of varieties of demonic influence, is at best acting presumptuously, and most certainly with cruelty.'[13]

Practical Help

Integrated help for the mentally ill has to go beyond kind words. Psychotherapy should not get bogged down in dialogue, and Pastoral Counselling should not exhaust itself in conversation. When Jesus described the great judgement at the end of time, he didn't ask those he was judging about their words, but about their deeds.[14] To the righteous he said, 'What you *did* to the least of these my brothers you did to me!' Love shown in actions can give the weak person the courage to once more face the everyday routine and risk stepping back into life. I would like to divide this practical help into three categories. Basically these are no different for someone with a psychiatric disorder than for someone with a broken leg.

1. Support
2. Mobilisation
3. Rehabilitation

1. *Support* You don't expect a person with a broken leg to start walking around straight away. He is given a plaster which supports the broken bone and holds it still to assist the healing process. It is the same with a mentally ill person, who feels overwhelmed by every bit of stress and sinks deeper into his suffering. *Support* then, means relieving the sick person of stresses, taking responsibilities from his shoulders and also doing little things for him. A depressive woman for instance could be helped with the housework, or you could look after her children for her. These 'simple' duties cannot be taken on either by the doctor, or other caring professionals. They have to rely on the help of the relatives and friends of their patients.

2. *Mobilisation* Once the ice of a depression begins gradually to melt, or the fire storm of a schizophrenic attack begins to die down, new seeds of life hesitantly start to grow again. At that point you need to get to know the sources of strength, the 'resources' which a patient has. By this we mean

the healthy parts of his personality, his interests and abilities, and also the opportunities for accommodation and work which will make return to normal life easier for him. These resources will be summed up in the framework of the treatment plan[15] and should also be taken note of by those who care outside the hospital.

Perhaps an interview with an employer is called for, or someone knows a family in the country who are prepared to take the sick person in to stay with them. In any case it is good if someone can take over the *co-ordination* of these efforts and plans and carry them through in consultation with the afflicted person and his relatives. It is necessary to stretch the sick person, without overstretching him. Demanding too much of a patient all at once can lead to great inner tension which may further unsettle his sensitive balance and trigger a relapse.

3.   *Rehabilitation*   In psychiatry we understand by this the re-integration and re-adaptation of a patient into business and private life after an illness.[16] Unfortunately in only a proportion of mentally ill people does rehabilitation mean complete restoration of the situation before the crisis. Often it is a question of helping the patient to live the most fulfilled life possible within the limitations of his disability. This task is nowadays recognised by social psychiatry, which has counselling centres in all the major cities. In co-operation with the welfare associations many arrangements have been made in recent years, especially residential homes and sheltered workshops, which promise to make the reintegration of psychiatrically handicapped people back into society much easier. Working on a Christian basis, a number of different therapeutic residential communities have joined together the form the Association of Christian Counselling in Germany and Switzerland. In Britain, information on similar activities can be obtained from CARE (Christian Action, Research and Education), 53 Romney Street, London SW1P 3RF, Tel. 081 233 0455.[17]

Don't forget the family

The relatives are often forgotten in the midst of efforts to help the patient. The psychiatrist only sees a sick person during the appointment but parents, brothers, sisters and the partner have to live with their sick relatives 24 hours a day. They suffer enormously as a result of the altered behaviour of their loved one which they find difficult to understand. Frequently they feel very much alone with feelings of rejection, guilt and helplessness.

For the relatives, the onset of schizophrenia is like entering a totally alien world in which they are turned loose without a map. It therefore must be a duty for the hospital staff, G.P.s and the pastoral counsellor as well, to take seriously the suffering endured by the relatives and to give them advice to help them in their difficult task.

In recent years the importance of the relatives in the treatment of psychiatric patients has been increasingly recognised.[18] They can meet in special groups for relatives to learn about the sickness and talk about their experiences and feelings. In reality the relatives often know more about the practical problems than do the doctors.

The way in which the relatives relate to their sick loved one ('expressed emotions') can contribute a great deal towards reducing tension and preventing relapses.[19] When they are supported and encouraged they find it easier to meet the sick person with the sympathy that is needed, and to stand by him even in the midst of an attack.

Help from Medication

Among lay people, by far the most controversial question is the use of drugs in connection with mental illnesses. All too often the long term use of psychopharmacy is seen by well-meaning helpers as equivalent to addiction and 'chemical dependence', and involving the suppression or alteration of the personality. As a result many sick people are caused to feel insecure and to leave off their medication. This frequently leads to a worsening of their situation.

I think of a young woman who had already been in hospital several times with attacks of schizophrenia. With regular medication she had made encouraging progress. She learned a trade, passed her driving test, found herself somewhere to live and began to work. She attended a young people's group and played an active part in her church. She had not needed a further stay in hospital for many years. She had a few minor bouts which had been controlled through supportive counselling sessions and adjustment of the dose of her medication.

But then she tried to 'live by faith' and gave up her medication. For a month everything went well. Then she became noticeably insecure, sensitive and driven. She lost her job, became confused and in the end had to be admitted to hospital again. The radiant Christian woman whom I had come to know during the counselling sessions presented a picture of misery. She had hoped to be 'free' without medication, but now she was again being ruled by her confused thoughts and was surrendered defenceless to her delusive fears.

Situations like this make me sad and often cause me to feel very discouraged, because the people who advise against medication are not usually around to find the patient a new job, pay for any damage they cause or care for them until they have dragged themselves back out of their relapse.

I would like to give one more reminder that psychopharmacy has made possible an increasing opening up of psychiatry, and that many psychiatric conditions have now lost their terror as a result of it. Three groups of drugs are available for the doctor to use in his treatment of psychiatric illness.

1. The *neuroleptic* drugs are the first line of attack in the treatment of psychoses.
2. The *antidepressants* have proved their worth in the treatment of depressions.
3. The *tranquillisers* (or benzodiazepines) have a

calming, relaxing, and anxiety-releasing effect, some of them induce sleep.

More detail concerning these drugs and their effects can be found in the descriptions of individual conditions in this book, and also in text books on psychopharmacology.[20] While some substances only need to be taken as a temporary measure in order to counter the effects of an attack, others, particularly the neuroleptics, have often to be administered over a period of years in order to prevent a relapse in people suffering from schizophrenia.

A Supplement to Pastoral Care

Nowadays medication stands alongside counselling and practical help as the third pillar of an integrated approach to treatment, for which even a Christian can be thankful. Medication can be valuable as a supplement to pastoral care. Often it is the medication in fact which improves the patient's situation to the extent that pastoral help becomes possible.

Understanding the biochemistry of the brain, which God created, enables us to understand many occurrences. I see no distinction between lifelong injection of insulin and the prolonged administration of drugs in the treatment of a psychosis. Whereas diabetes is caused by a disorder of the metabolism of the pancreas, in the other case, administration of other drugs leads to an improvement in the metabolism of the brain.

Nevertheless, the *difficulties involved in psychopharmacy* should not be played down. Many aspects of the way that drugs work remain unclear. Many conditions have so far not responded to medication. All drugs are not equally effective or indeed necessary. And unfortunately there are always patients who suffer as a result of disturbing side-effects. Finally, the danger of dependency, especially from sleeping tablets and tranquillisers, should not be played down. Nevertheless, a pastoral counsellor should not under any circumstances advise a client to set aside his medication, without consulting with the doctor. With the background of his training and experience, the doctor is the only one who can estimate when medication is advisable, or when a change in the medication is possible.

Preventive Care

Treatment is good, but prevention is better! This statement is valid to a special degree where psychiatric problems are concerned. So to conclude this chapter we will ask what possibilities are open to the christian denominations and local churches to help in the prevention of psychiatric disorders. The potential of a live christian fellowship is often undervalued. Many ministers, preachers and church workers are never aware of the important contribution made by their work and their preaching towards the prevention of sicknesses of the soul. In an article in an academic journal two American professors of psychology demonstrated the significance of the Christian church in the framework of psycho-social endeavours.[21] In this context they distinguished three forms of prevention.

1. *Primary Prevention*. This meets needs and offers help in such a way as to impede the development of psychiatric disorders. Various psychological studies have indicated that two factors contribute to this:
   a) Awareness of meaning and purpose in life and
   b) Social contact and viable family relationships which come alongside to give a person support through the difficult circumstances of life. Both needs can be met in an ideal way through live Christianity.
2. *Secondary Prevention*. This consists in the early recognition and treatment of developing psychiatric problems. This reduces the severity and duration of the disorder and eventually makes hospitalisation unnecessary.

At this stage a church member may well consult a doctor and perhaps even require medication. But this will be undergirded by sympathetic care on the part of friends and helpers in the church.

3. *Tertiary Prevention.* This comes into play after a nervous breakdown or after a stay in hospital and helps the sick person to find their way back into everyday life. Impartial, uncondemning acceptance by people in the housegroup and congregation is of great significance at this point, allowing the person to experience love and acceptance in spite of their past rejection and their present limitations.

I can think of no better basis for integrated treatment and prevention of psychiatric disorders than the power and motivation which spring from Christian faith. If Christians are willing to let themselves be trained in this sphere, if they learn to view their suffering fellow human beings with eyes of compassion and active love, they can make an invaluable contribution to the integrated treatment of psychiatric illness.

CHAPTER THIRTEEN

LIVING WITH LIMITATIONS

*I*n our time, people are always looking for quick and easy solutions. Immediate and complete healing—such is the goal of society in the 20th century. Modern medicine evidently makes this possible. Fast acting drugs, daring operations and electronic aids have pushed death and suffering to the back stage of physical illness. On top of this, when medicine fails, practitioners of alternative medicine and spiritual healers offer their help with the promise of a miraculous cure.

Even Christians are affected by the power-crazed attitude of our time. Healing is the only valid sign of genuine faith and only signs and wonders reflect the work of God. It is the spectacular successes which hit the headlines, not the patiently born suffering in homes for the chronically sick and the long-stay wards of psychiatric hospitals. The triumphs of physical medicine and the proud promises of healers of every kind often cause us to overlook the fact that suffering which takes a tedious course without dramatic improvement still remains with us.

Five Stages of Grief

Fortunately many psychiatric disorders consist in one temporary attack during a lifetime, which rights itself in the course of time and lingers only as a distant dark memory. But in many cases the mental changes which are involved set the points for the sick person and their relatives to switch to another life, shaped by the disability, which is difficult to bear. It is as if you have to endure a parting from the person you used to know. It takes time to come to accept a life with limitations. Hardly anyone has the ability to make the adjustment sensibly and in a mature way from one day to the next. Often five phases can be discerned in the reaction of patients and their relatives:

1. Negation and concealment
2. Search for causes and apportionment of blame or self-condemnation
3. Desperate search for help and healing
4. Insecurity and resignation
5. Acceptance and re-establishment of relationships.

The person who understands this grieving process will find it easier to work with the sick person and his relatives without reproaching them for their reactions which can be difficult to understand at the best of times. For this reason we will briefly examine each of the steps.

1. *Negation and Concealment*: To begin with it is difficult for most people to accept a mental illness in themselves or their loved ones. They cannot and will not believe it. Often they desperately try to hide it from friends and neighbours. Along with this goes a characteristic shame which allows the existence of a mentally-ill relative to become a secret which they expose only with reluctance. But this makes the inward tension even worse.

2. *Search for Causes, Blaming or Self-Condemnation*: The speechlessness of the initial shock is released by digging over the causes of the illness. While one person will project the blame outwards (from the 'mother who didn't love him' to 'demonic oppression') another will lay the blame on themselves. How many parents agonise over questions like 'where did we go wrong in bringing

up our child?' Reproaches are also directed
towards the hospital and those who are caring for
the patient, especially when the desired
improvement doesn't come as quickly as
expected. This difficult behaviour is easier to put
up with, when it is seen as an expression of the
insecurities of relatives who themselves are at the
end of their tether.

3. *Desperate Search for Help and Healing*:
For many people it is simply unbearable to watch
helplessly while their loved one's personality
changes. They are on the receiving end of
thousands of words of advice as to how they can
help the sick person. These come from friends,
neighbours, and fellow-Christians, and can give
rise to an unhelpful tug of war between helpers
which can harm the sick person rather than helping
him.

4. *Insecurity and Resignation*: With the passage of
time, in the face of the futility of all the efforts,
helplessness and hopelessness begin to take hold.
Interviews with doctors and social workers, as well
as pastoral counsellors and lay helpers do not
always bring any relief. One mother complained
'what else can I do for my son? Whatever I do, it's
always wrong'.

5. *Acceptance and Re-establishment of Relationships*:
It often takes months and years until the afflicted
person can accept the new limitations, and until
relatives can lay aside their reproaches and self-
condemnation and learn to live with him.

Can Faith Give Support?

These phases of grief are to be observed equally among
committed Christians. It is only natural that, like anyone else,
as weak human beings, Christians will threaten to break down
under the pressure of a burden suddenly placed on their

shoulders. As Paul once put it so strikingly, 'The burden I had to carry was more than I could bear. I had no hope any longer . . . ' However, his testimony doesn't finish at this point. He continues 'But this happened so that I wouldn't rely on myself, but only on God . . . '.[1] The Bible doesn't lie about the reality of suffering. On the other hand, it doesn't stop at a stoical endurance of the inevitable . . . it points to the comfort and power in suffering which finds its ultimate meaning in God. Faith can give support. Not only does the Bible bear witness to this message, it is repeated every day by people who turn to God for help.

I am moved time and time again by interviews with the relatives of my chronically ill patients. I can still vividly remember the elderly parents of a psychiatrically disabled man who required care from them day and night on account of his fears and compulsions. They were often at the end of their tether, and yet they always seemed so confident. I asked them what gave them the ability to cope. They answered: 'Our friends, the help the doctors give, and above all our daily prayer—time where we can unload our cares to God. If we didn't have God, we don't know what we would do.'

Faith Healing

While one person will claim God's help to cope in the every day situation, many Christians look for more: They hope for a *miracle* from God—not simply getting through, but complete healing of the sick person through faith. What gives them the power to cope is hoping for God's supernatural intervention.

Doctors and lay people, psychiatrists and pastoral counsellors, have different definitions of what they would describe as a miracle.[2] The doctors tend to apply rigorous scientific standards and only to accept as a miracle a situation where a sick person is completely healed against all odds. This definition of 'miracle' has also been taken on board in many Christian circles. That raises the question: 'Is God only at work when someone becomes in every degree as capable of work and just as happy as they were before? This approach holds within it the danger of squeezing God into a mould which, in spite of Christian rhetoric, lies nearer to the success mentality of the world than to what the Bible says about God's purposes with weak, suffering people.[3]

It cannot be denied that miraculous healings do still happen today, where illnesses take a course which goes against all human expectations.[4] But often these do not come about as dramatic changes under the spotlight of a special healing service. Even today, God meets people as he once met discouraged Elijah,[5] not so much in the tempest of a great meeting as in the soft breeze of a gradual healing in the stillness.

With many people who have told me about miracles in their life, I discovered in addition a wider outlook on miracles, which is not covered by the strict medical view. As a result nowadays I tend to see complete restoration as only the highest level of the miraculous. God's work is manifold. His miracles take place on a daily basis in a broad spectrum between the extremes of all and nothing. The experience of a miracle is personal to an individual or maybe a group of people who have got together to pray for a sick person. For them a supernatural healing takes place when they experience God's intervention in a serious situation in response to their prayers, even if the change is not a lasting one. I recall a young woman who struggled under the most severe depressions and after months in hospital without any noticeable improvement was taken home again by her parents. Her mental abilities had declined to a point where she could hardly carry out a simple task for more than an hour. Yet gradually her situation became brighter, indeed, she improved to the point where she was able to take an apprenticeship and tackle a whole day's work in a sheltered workshop. Now she had recovered her radiance. Within her new limitations she had found meaning for her life. She no longer seemed to be the same person I had previously got to know in the hospital. 'Doctor,' the parents said to me, 'what has happened to our

daughter is a miracle. The doctors gave us no hope that it
could ever improve, and now she is doing so well!' I had to
agree with them, even though from a strictly medical point of
view, I knew that such remissions can take place, and a year
later I had to treat the daughter again during the course of a
further attack.

Often God does not just alter the afflicted person's
physical condition but also their inward attitude to life and to
the sickness. He walks patiently with the patient and his
relatives and friends along the pathway of the bereavement
process from the stage of rebellion against the illness to the
point where they begin to re-establish their life. And that in
itself is a gift, indeed, a miracle from God.

The Limitations of the Possible

But what happens when there is no noticeable
improvement —when no great miracle takes place? Are there
still answers to the questions which are raised by those who
are weak in soul and their relatives? Do doctors and
counsellors still have hope and help to offer?

The goal of complete mental health often becomes a
hindrance in effective long term care. Not a few helpers—
psychotherapists as well as Christians committed to pastoral
care—are shipwrecked on the rocks of chronic illness. When
the goal is set too high, failures are programmed in to the
situation and are difficult for pastoral counsellors and
therapists alike to cope with. Some will feel they themselves
have failed. Others will lay the blame on the sick person and
their environment, but that benefits no-one.

In their helplessness they grasp at the most diverse
theories and magical ideas about the causes of psychiatric
illness. Sentences are to be heard over and over again
which in many forms always include the same few words: 'If
only . . . then!' *If only* he had kept to his diet, *if only* he had
been able to scream out his inner wounds, *if only* he had
believed the right things, *then* he would have been healed. All
of these methods have their significance, but the excessive

application of them to people who are weak and suffering from psychiatric illness brings nothing but tears of disappointment.

Only when helpers and patients learn to accept the reality of human weakness and the limitations of the possible, when they learn to endure the tensions of incompleteness and of those aspects of this life which are ultimately unexplainable, only then is effective long-term care a possibility.[6] The 'why?' of suffering is still one of the most difficult questions facing mankind. Even the Christian is not promised a problem-free life on this earth. He lives in a world where he painfully runs into boundaries from time to time. He is afflicted by 'troubles', experiences 'trials' and has 'burdens' to bear. Neither the best therapy nor the most biblical pastoral care can remove these limitations. Change and healing cannot be 'produced'.

I would like to point out four important underlying causes for these limitations:

1. *The nature of fallen creation.* Pain, fear and suffering are part of the substance of our early life. Paul describes vividly the anxious suffering of the created world, its mortality and its longing for redemption in a new world.[7] Biblical pastoral counselling also has to come to terms with this fact and draw it into a comprehensive approach.

2. *The nature of physical illness.* Like the other organs of the body the brain (and hence also the *psyche*) is subject to mortality and weakness, by which Christians are also afflicted, through no fault of their own. So it is necessary for us to accept patients with severe disorders once they have been sorted out, and help and support them.

3. *Fallen human nature.* Even when a person is healthy from a psychiatric point of view, they will only be able to cope with a limited alteration to their lifestyle. They have received freewill from

God as the greatest of his gifts. As a result, the best advice achieves nothing, even among patients who are capable of conversation, unless they are able and willing to put it into effect.

4. *The limitations of our knowledge.* Not only in psychiatry, but also in relationship to the significance of biblical pastoral care. The dilemma of contradictory explanations for the causes and therapy of psychiatric problems affects the Christian therapist as much as any other, and demands that we show humility and keep an open heart when we encounter new theories.

Weakness: God's power in earthen vessels

I can well understand that these thoughts may awaken feelings of helplessness in the reader, perhaps feelings of discouragement and even of rage. Establishing these limitations calls the philosophy of life of many Christians into question. Many readers will contradict me, with some justification, by saying: 'What use is the Faith, if it cannot remove suffering? If Christianity cannot bring release from depression and mental disorders, then what else can?' It is at this point, however, that rethinking has to start. A new approach to life, inspired by trust in God, can grow at precisely the point where an attitude directed basically to this life falls apart. The Bible not only shows us the limitations of our existence, it also shows us how deeply valuable human beings are, even in our weakness.

God's power in the weakness and suffering of this world—the theme runs through the gospel story. Even the prophets began to describe the coming Messiah in a way which didn't fit the prevailing attitude of the world which was based on beauty and success, on wealth and power. Christ unites in Himself both the shining glory of Heaven and the stuffy constriction of the stable in Bethlehem, the absolute power of the judge of all the earth, and the mercy of the reconciling high priest;[9] He is the holy God and a 'Friend of sinners'[10] He lives in 'a high and holy place', but also with those who are contrite and lowly in spirit, to revive the spirit of the lowly and to revive the heart of the contrite.'[11] He drives the tradesman out of the temple by force, but 'a bruised reed he will not break, and a smouldering wick he will not snuff out.'[12]

The Bible represents a picture of the human condition radically different from that which the contemporary standard of this world has in view. Jesus is on the side of the weak. God often chooses not to reveal himself through what is strong, but rather to work through those who are aware of their weakness.[13] The *weak person* gains his value in the first place, not from his achievements, but from trusting in God's grace.

In his second letter to the Corinthians, Paul uses a wonderful picture to illustrate this fact. He describes the weak person as a *vessel made of clay* in which God keeps his 'costly treasure to show that this all-surpassing power is from God, and not from us,' and he continues:

> 'We are hard pressed on every side, but not crushed; perplexed, but not in despair; persecuted, but not abandoned; struck down, but not destroyed . . . therefore we do not lose heart. Though outwardly we are wasting away, yet inwardly we are being renewed day by day.
> For our light and momentary troubles are achieving for us an eternal glory that far outweighs them all. So we fix our eyes not on what is seen, but on what is unseen. For what is seen is temporary, but what is unseen is eternal.'[15]

Here we encounter a genuine ability to cope with life and a real hope, which reach far beyond a one-sided desire for external healing. Christians who take God's Word seriously will not simply fold their hands in their lap in resignation. They are receiving extra strength from a new source. For them, healing is much more than mere external change. Their hope remains even when natural energies have been exhausted. If doctors, pastoral counsellors and fellow human beings see the person with a psychiatric illness from this perspective, then his weakness takes on a practical function, as was described in the previous chapter. They become fellow-workers in undergirding the process which God Himself initiates and which renews the weak person's strength from day to day, even when he has to live with limitations.

The outward limitations often open up a new inner freedom. Where rebellion against the disability stops, a person's energies can be gathered for inner growth. Viktor Frankl, the founder of Logotherapy, once observed: 'Life proves to be basically meaningful, even if it is neither creative nor rich in experience. There are values which can only be discovered as people adjust themselves to a restriction of their life. In their personal response to this restriction of their autonomy lies the key to open up a new and unique realm of values which certainly belong to the highest of all.'[16]

A fresh glimpse of hope

'Is there still hope?' How often doctors are bombarded with this question by patients and relatives alike! Frequently, before I answer, I myself first pose a counter-question: 'What does 'hope' mean for you?' Do you mean hope of a cure through psychiatry? Hope of healing through God's intervention, or just hope of some improvement in the condition?

Often patients and their relatives on the one hand, and doctors on the other, are not speaking the same language. As a result people talk too often of a 'hopeless case', simply because it does not fit the category of hope for complete restoration. But there are no hopeless cases with God. Faith cannot always provide complete mental health, but it can provide strength and comfort in the midst of weakness, fear and feelings of rejection. The Bible points to a hope that reaches beyond the helplessness of our earthly existence to give people courage to bear the simply unbearable. At the very point where doctor and pastoral counsellor, medical staff and lay helpers alike run against the barrier of external things that cannot be changed . . . at that point, in God's eyes fresh doors open.

I am often asked: what hope can you offer your patients as a psychiatrist and as a Christian? I would like to divide my answer into two main areas, namely the medical-human perspective (1–5) and the biblical point of view (6–10)

1. I have hope for people with psychiatric problems and illnesses, because experience shows that most disorders abate after a certain time.[17]

2. I have hope, because today, in comparison with earlier times, the suffering involved in psychiatric illness can be moderated or even healed through the help of medication in many more situations than was previously the case.

3. I have hope, because psychiatric problems often provide the opportunity for a new beginning. A crisis in a person's life may be needed, in order for him to recognise the fragile basis of his existence and build his life on new, firm foundations.

4. I have hope, because I have experienced in many cases that people can live a fulfilled life, even with a psychiatric weakness. This applies even with people who have pronounced changes of their personality. Even if they have to undergo very difficult experiences, they usually find the way through to a new life within their limitations, after the passage of time.

5. I have hope, because initiatives are increasingly taking place today to provide residential homes and work opportunities for people suffering from

psychiatric illness, in order to ease their lot and support them in shaping their life. In this connection relatives' support groups also bring hope for those who are afflicted and their families.

However, my hope goes beyond these medical and human considerations. Only the person who knows God's presence and his promises has ultimate hope.

6. So, I have hope, since it continually remains true that 'all things work together for the good of those who love God',[18] even when we are prevented for much of the time from looking behind the curtains of suffering to see what is really going on. A woman with a son who was severely ill once said to me:'I keep hoping, because I know God doesn't make any mistakes.'

7. I have hope, because God can do miracles when he wants to. In the letter to the Ephesians it says 'God can do far more exceeding abundantly above all that we can ask for or even think of, so great is His power which is at work within us'.[19] Sometimes the miracle is already there in the fact that the people who are afflicted and their relatives do not succumb to bitter resignation.

8. I have hope because God loves and accepts people with psychiatric weaknesses, even if they cannot completely grasp this truth and express it in words.[20]

9. I have hope, because God can even work through weakness. He pours His power into 'earthly vessels' and says to the weak person: 'my grace is all you need, because my power is made perfect in weakness.'[21]

10. Finally, I have hope, because our existence in this world is not to be compared with the eternal life

which God promises to those who put their trust in him. Paul writes:

'I consider that our present sufferings are not worth comparing with the glory that will be revealed in us'.[22]

Supporting and being supported

In these ten statements lies hope not only for the weak, but also for those who help to carry their burdens. God alone knows how much we can cope with and for how long. He not only helps in the weakness of the person needing help, but also in the weakness of the helper. He grants 'the serenity to accept the things which I cannot change, the courage to change the things I can, and the wisdom to know the difference.'[23]

It is my hope that this book will give you the courage to bear those burdens which God has allowed to remain in your life. And my desire is that you may learn to know the strength of the One who gently draws near in times of discouragement, putting Himself alongside you under the cross your life gives you to bear: namely Jesus Christ, who calls people, saying 'Come to me all who are weary and burdened, and I will give you rest. Take my yoke upon you and learn from me, for I am gentle and humble in heart, and you will find rest for you souls. For my yoke is easy and my burden is light.'[24]

Because He puts himself under the yoke with us, we can both fulfil our practical responsibilities in everyday life, and also find rest in the knowledge that *He* rather than we, has the final responsibility for the success of our efforts. Being rooted in God sets the helper free to be open for others, a thought which is strikingly expressed in an old prayer:

> Lord, open my eyes,
> To wonder at your glory
> And see the need of my fellow human beings.

Lord, open my ears,
To receive your word
And hear the cry of the poor.

Lord, open my lips,
That my mouth may proclaim your praise
And find kind words to say.

Lord open my heart,
So that I may have room for you
And welcome everyone I meet.

ENDNOTES

Introduction

1. Kielholz, 1981.

2. Hufeland, quoted by Will, 1985.

3. Häfner, 1985.

4. On the other hand the total number of mentally ill people is increasing as a result of higher life expectancy. This is especially the case with the mentally handicapped, chronic mental illness and senile dementia.

5. c.f. Hemminger, 'Psychotherapie—Weg zum Glück?' (Psychotherapy—way to happiness?), 1987.

6. c.f. his article 'Religion—die letzte Tabu? Uber die Verdrängung der Religiosität in Psychologie, Psychiatrie und Psychotherapie' (Religion—the last taboo, concerning the suppression of religion in psychology, psychiatry and psychotherapy) in Kung, 1987, pp. 111–142.

7. Blankenburg and Zilly, 1973.

8. Bleuler, 1975, p.399.

9. Books by Oates, 1980, Maymann 1984 and Nohl 1981 describe notable exceptions.

10. Küng, 1987, p. 140.

1. Psychiatry Under Fire

1. Hell, 1987, p. 87.

2. Will, 1985.

3. Zilbergeld, 1983.

4. For e.g. Zilbergeld, 1983 or Hemminger, 1985.

5. Weyerer and Dilling, 1984.

6. For example Michel and Spengler (Hg), 1985.

7. For example Adams, 1972, Cosgrove, 1979 and Dieterich, 1984.

8. Compare Vitz, 1977.

9. Ernst, 1984.

10. Pfeifer, 1985.

11. Matthew 16:25–26; Hebrews 6:19; Ephesians 6:6.

12. For example in 1 Corinthians 16:19.

13. Hampden-Turner, gives a good over-view of the 'Model of the Human Being', 1982.

14. Recommended text books of Psychiatry are 'Tolle', 1982, 'Feldman', 1984 and 'Bleuler', 1975.

15. Schmidbauer, 1977.

16. Schmidbauer, 1983.

17. The handbook produced by Sass and Köhler 'Diagnostisches und Statistisches Manual psychischer Störungen' (Diagnostic and statistical manual of psychiatric disorders), DSM 111, will provide an important grounding here, 1984.

18. 'Der Spiegel', 47, 1978.

19. 'Der Spiegel', 44, 1983.

20. Compare with Braun, 1981, Ernst and Ernst, 1986.

21. A comprehensive discussion can be found in Ernst, 1986.

22. cf. Küng, pp. 111–145, 1987.

2. *The Image of Human Nature in Psychiatry*

1. I am aware, that I also am being selective here and that my selection is incomplete. However, I have at least tried to arrange the psychotherapists as evenly around the elephant as I can.

2. Miller, 1982.

3. Watson, p. 147.

4. Lazarus, 1985, Hennenhofer, 1975.

5. Beck, 1981.

6. Adams, 1972.

7. For instance in Ephesians 4:22–24.

8. Proverbs 4:23 (Good News Bible).

9. Colossians 3:2.

10. Colossians 3:16.

11. Backus, 1983, Stoop, 1982, Wright, 1981. Tan gives a good overview, 1987.

12. Ellis, 1977.

13. Lazarus, 1985.

14. Maslow, 1968.

15. Rogers, 1983.

16. Rogers, 1977.

17. Willi, p. 20, 1985.

18. Ebenda, p. 23.

19. Hemminger, 1985.

20. Oden, 1974, Gassmann, 1984.

21. The new books by Robert Schuller are the most well-known, but there are also beginnings among the German speaking people, for example Becker, 1982.

22. Crabb, p. 133ff., 1985.

23. Müller, 1984.

24. Walsh and Vaughan, 1980.

25. Rohner, 1985.

26. Haller, 1983.

27. Dethlefsen, 1976.

28. Sufficient information about the underlying 'New Age' philosophy may be found in König, 1986, and Ruppert, 1985.

29. Thurneysen, 1980.

30. 1 Thessalonians 5:21.

31. Crabb, pp. 47–51, 1984.

32. Jaspers, p. 685, 1959.

3. The Miracle of the Human Brain

1. Eccles, p. 18, 1979.

2. Poeldinger, 1982.

3. Psychologie Heute (Psychology Today), p. 8, January 1986.

4. An outstanding, illustrated summary of the research findings described in this chapter, written in an easily understood way, can be found in the GEO-Wissen-Heft, 1987, with the title 'Brain, feeling, thought' (Gehirn, Gefühl, Gedanken). Almost as easy to understand is the book by Restak, 1985. In the remarks that follow, I lean heavily on Eccles, 1979, Lausch, 1974, Jones, 1981, as well as an article by Begley and others, 1983. In addition information comes from scientific literature, which is not cited here.

5. Comprehensive information about the uses and abuses of brain surgery can be found in Koch, 1978.

6. Pardes, 1986, provides a scientifically based overview with many references to corresponding academic works. Of special interest is an account by Sedvall and others, 1986, which describes techniques for making neurotransmitters visible in the brain of living people.

7. Haefely and Möhler, 1980.

8. Lit Angststoff. Science 227:934.

9. Bräutigam, 1981.

10. Knoll, 1984.

11. Holaday, 1984.

12. Pribham, 1986, Süllwold, 1988, Huber and Süllwold, 1986.

13. Comprehensive scientific discussions concerning the significance of spirit and brain can be found in Eccles and Popper, 1982, Pribham, 1986, and Searle, 1984. In addition, Collins, 1985, Jones, 1981 and Cosgrove, 1977, give thorough presentations from a Christian point of view.

14. I use the concept of 'the spirit' here, although one would certainly also speak about the soul. Neidhart, 1985, has opened up the question of the dual or tri-partite nature, in a valuable theological work.

4. How Mental Disorders Develop

1. Rainer gives a comprehensive review, 1980.

2. Science 234:1324.

3. Helpful multi-dimensional personality analyses can be achieved by means of the Freiburg Personality Indicator (FPI), The Taylor - Johnson Temperament Analysis (TJTA), as well as the Minnesota Multi-phasic Personality Inventory (MMPI), so long as one is aware of the limitations of the resulting descriptions.

4. Eysenck and Kamin, 1981.

5. Kagan, 1987, McFarlane, 1964.

6. 1 Thessalonians 5:14.

7. 2 Cornthians 12:9–10.

8. Ernst and Von Luckner, 1985.

9. Hemminger, 1982.

10. Ebenda, p. 212.

11. Ebenda.

12. 2 Corinthians 6:4.

13. Galatians 6:2.

14. 1 Peter 1:6.

15. 1 Corinthians 10:13.

16. Examples can be found in Psalms 22, 25, 31, 38, 71, 73 and many others.

17. 2 Corinthians 4:8–9.

18. A thorough discussion can be found in Frank, 1985.

19. For example in Romans 8:6 and 12:2; Philippians 2:5 (RSV).

20. For example in Ephesians 4:22, Galatians 1:13.

21. Proverbs 4:23.

22. Galatians 5:16.

23. Ephesians 4:15.

24. Ephesians 4:15.

25. Ephesians 4:24.

26. Psalm 77:3–11.

27. Romans 8:26–27.

5. Neurotic Disorders—An Overview

1. Tölle, p. 54, 1982.

2. Dilling, 1981.

3. Especially the 'Diagnostische und Statistiche Manual Psychischer Storungen DSM 111' (Diagnostic and

Statistical Manual of Psychiatric Disorders DSM 111)
published by Sass and Köhler, 1984.

4. Bräutigam, quoted by Mester and Todle, p. 2, 1981.

5. Ernst, p. 222, 1981.

6. Hemminger, 1982, Eschenrödter, p. 91 ff., 1984.

7. Schepank, 1974.

8. With a few patients extremely stressful experiences can
   certainly be established, which in their case have led to
   the outbreak or worsening of their suffering. On the
   other hand with others, no such connection can be
   established. To date there are only a few control studies
   on this theme. One exampl.e can be found in Roy, Byrne
   and others, 1986.

9. In psychoanalysis the term 'Defence mechanism' is used
   in this connection. This concept is very helpful in the
   understanding of neurotic behaviour and has been
   comprehensively described for example by Anna Freud,
   1984.

10. The literature bemoans the increase of the 'grey
    illnesses' which are characterised by diffuse suffering,
    vague and somatised anxiety, restlessness and inability to
    work. This fact has been enough from the pathological
    point of view, for the creation of new syndromes, for e.g.
    the Borderline Disorder and the Narcissistic disorder, and
    from the point of view of diagnosis, the possibility of the
    multiaxial description of syndromes in DSM 111, cf.
    Tolle et al., 1987.

6. Anxiety, Obsessive Compulsive and Hystrionic Disorders

1.   Riemann, 1975.

2.   Relaxation can be produced by the most varied methods.
     A herbal tea, a long walk or a warm bath can release
     inner tension. Others attempt to gain relaxation through
     the use of the mind alone. At this point Christians have
     to ask themselves whether they can harmonise the
     suggestions of a technique (for example the higher levels
     of autogenic training) with their faith. Dieterich, has
     indicated interesting alternatives from a Christian
     viewpoint, 1984.

3.   This is impressively documented in the book 'Wenn
     Psychotherapien Schaden' by Hemminger and Becker,
     which is well worth reading, 1985.

4.   Marks, 1985, Rickels et al., 1985.

5.   John 16:33.

6.   The newer programmes by Süllwold and Huber, for basic
     cognitive disturbances can also be applied in an adapted
     form to severe neuroses, 1986.

7.   cf. Riemann, pp. 156 ff., 1975.

8.   The term 'Borderline Disorder' has been used in an
     attempt to describe the boundaries observed between
     neuroses and psychoses. This diagnosis is however the
     cause of much contention, and will not be thoroughly
     explained in this book. Further literature can be found in
     Sass and Koehler, 1983, Perry and Klerman, 1978, as
     well as Gmür, 1986.

9. Conversely, hysterical forms of behaviour can also occur in relation to depression, as you will find demonstrated with impressive examples in an article by Garcia and Sander, 1983.

10. Benedetti has provided a brilliant analysis of correct pastoral treatment from a psycho-analytic point of view using the example of Blumhardt's struggle with Dittus, 1960.

11. Hark, 1984; Evangelical Christians will not be able to go along all the way with the author's arguments, which are influenced by Jungian Psychology. Nevertheless, I think he has produced a valuable contribution to the theme of religious neuroses, which is complemented by a comprehensive bibliography.

12. Ebenda, p. 209 ff.

13. Ebenda, p. 12 ff.

14. Helpful books on this theme are provided by Scharrer, 1984, Tournier, (undated) and McClung, 1986.

15. Blumhardt, p. 84, 1968.

7. *Depression—An Overview*

1. Baker and Nester provide an impressive portrayal of a severe depression, 1986. The best overview from a Christian standpoint is that by White, 1987.

2. Modified from DSM 111, published by Sass and Köhler, 1984.

3. Kielholz, Poldinger and Adams, 1981.

4. After Beck, 1981.

5. A scientific summary can be found in Akiskal and McKinney, 1975. The book by Battegay is also valuable, 1985.

6. P. Strauch gives an impressive portrayal of this, 1982.

7. Comprehensive epidemiological data was gathered in the researches of J. Angst in Zurich. A full report can be found for example in a work published by Angst in 1983.

8. Keller et al, 1986, and Laux, 1986.

9. The most comprehensive account of depressive delusions is to be found in Von Orelli, 1954.

10. Manics are not always affected in a happy and cheerful way, however. Not a few manic patients become tense, surly and bad-tempered in their driven state, and perceive themselves as surrounded by frustrating hindrances to their hyperactivity.

8. Severe Depression

1. A very valuable scientific investigation was opened up by Hole, 1977.

2. After Kielholz and Adams, 1981.

3. A valuable collection of Bible promises is contained in the little book 'Fester als Felsen' (Firmer than Rock). Published by Schulte and Gerth, Asslar, 1983.

4. A comprehensive account of avoidable mistakes in diagnosis and therapy can be found in a book of that name by Kielholz and Adams, 1984.

5. cf. for example Micah 7:8, 'Through I have fallen, I will arise, though I sit in darkness, the Lord will be my light'.

6. 1 John 3:20.

7. In Psalm 73:23, for example.

8. Simons et al., 1984.

9. Comprehensive information about antidepressive treatment is given for example by Poldinger and Wider, 1986.

10. Further information about the treatment of endogenous depression with Lithium can be found in the valuable little book by Schou, 1978. It is written in language which can be understood equally well by doctor and patient alike.

11. After Poeldinger, 1982/2.

12. Blackburn, 1986.

13. A comprehensive summary can be found in Reimer, 1982.

14. Reimer gives a full presentation, 1982.

15. Legal cases concerning liability when a suicide takes place in a hospital are becoming more and more frequent. Mauz gave an impressive account, 1986.

9. Schizophrenia—An Overview

1. For example Tölle, 1982, Feldmann, 1984.

2. Modified in accordance with the criteria of the DSM III, published by Sass and Köhler, 1984.

3. Müller et al., 1986.

4. Süllwold, 1977, Huber, 1983.

5. Compare especially here the work of Scharfetter, 1986.

6. Ciompi, 1981.

7. Weiner, 1980.

8. Phelps, 1985.

9. Hartmann et al., 1977 and 1983.

10. After Zubin et al., 1977 and 1983.

11. Examples can be found in Begley, 1983, Grove, 1985, Neuchterlein, 1984.

10. Schizophrenia and Faith

1. A valuable study on the theme of 'Superstition, Faith and Delusion' was published by von Haenel, 1983. The Munich psychologist Huth looks into the boundaries between 'Faith, ideology and delusion', 1984.

2. Zweifel and Scharfetter, 1977, Kohler, 1978.

3. Zweifel and Scharfetter, p. 320, 1977.

4. Kranz, 1955 and 1967.

5. Blankenburg and Zilly, 1973, von Orelli, 1954.

6. Adams, p. 28ff., 192.

7. Margies, part II, p. 220ff., 1983.

8. Ebenda, p. 231.

11. Schizophrenia—Therapy and Pastoral Care

1. Green, 1964.

2. Koenigsberg and Handley, 1986.

3. Drake and Sederer, 1986, and Gunderson et al., 1984.

4. Margies II, p. 228 as well as my own observations, 1983.

5. With reliance on Horie, 1978.

6. Romans 8:26.

7. Galatians 6:2.

12. Integrated Care of the Mentally Ill

1. Poeldinger, 1984.

2.   cf. Chapter 13: Living with limitations.

3.   1 Thessalonians 5:14.

4.   cf. the heading 'Geduld' in Coenen et al., p. 463, 1983.

5.   Proverbs 16:24 (Good News Bible).

6.   Proverbs 18:20–21 (Everyday Bible—New Century Version).

7.   Matthew 9:36 (NIV).

8.   The Greek word at this point signifies 'The strongest feeling of compassionate, for e.g. loving . . . attention.' cf. heading 'Barmherzigkeit' in Coenen et al., p. 57, 1983.

9.   Matthew 12:7.

10. James 1:19 (NIV).

11. The book by Egan gives valuable guidance for counselling sessions, 1984.

12. I have dealt comprehensively elsewhere with the question of 'Occult bondage in the tension between pastoral counselling and psychiatry' (Okkulten Belastung im Spannungsfeld zwischen Seelsorge und Psychiatrie), Pfeifer, 1987.

13. Lechler, p. 83, 1978.

14. Matthew 25:34–35.

15. Needham has produced a helpful book on the planning of psychiatric care, 1987.

16. A good overview can be found in VanHout, 1988.

17. The individual works were published in a small book by ACL, 1985.

18. Hell wrote about the new developments in working with relatives, 1987. Dorner wrote an impressive plea for the involvement of relatives in therapy, 1982. Finally, a valuable introduction to working with relatives stems from Fiedler et al., 1986.

19. More about this concept can be found in Fiedler, pp. 78ff., 1986.

20. For example in the handy little book by Heinrich, 1983.

21. Bufford and Johnson, 1982, similar statements can be found in Collins, pp. 189–205, 1979.

13. Living with Limitations

1. 2 Corinthians 1:8–9.

2. Lewis has produced a very helpful work concerning the meaning of the term 'Miracle' from a scientific and theological point of view, 1980.

3. A comprehensive discussion of this question can be found in Farah, 1984.

4. cf. the report by Müller, 1985.

5. 1 Kings 19:11–13.

6. An extremely helpful and academically outstanding analysis of these interconnections was published by

Bennett and Bennett under the provocative title: 'The Uses of Hopelessness', 1984.

7.   Romans 8:18–25.

8.   Many valuable books deal with the problem of suffering in the context of pastoral care. Especially worthy of recommendation are Schaeffer, 1986, Yancey, 1979, Vanauken and Lewis, 1980.

9.   Hebrews 4:14–16.

10.   Luke 7:34.

11.   Isaiah 57:15.

12.   Isaiah 42:3.

13.   This concept of power in weakness is especially to the fore in the Pauline epistles. The american theologian, Black, gives a good overview, 1984.

14.   2 Corinthians 4:7.

15.   2 Corinthians 4:8–9, 16–18 (NIV).

16.   Frankl, p. 61, 1983.

17.   In describing the individual conditions I have provided some information about the statistics for the course of the illnesses. These show that, seen from an overall point of view, it is only in a small proportion of the sick people that a really severe chronic state develops.

18.   Romans 8:28.

19.   Ephesians 3:20.

20. Romans 8:26.

21. 2 Corinthians 12:9.

22. Romans 8:18 (NIV).

23. After a prayer ascribed to Oetinger, quoted by Nohl, p. 209, 1981.

24. Matthew 11:28–30.

BIBLIOGRAPHY

ACL (1985) Leben will gelernt sein. Die Arbeitsgemeinschaft Christlicher Lebenshilfen (ACL) stellt sich vor. Schulte und Gerth, Asslar.

Adams JE (1972) Befreiende Seelsorge. Theorie und Praxis einer biblischen Lebensberatung. Brunnen-Verlag, Basel/Gießen.

Akiskal AS, McKinney TW (1975) Overview of recent research in depression. Archives of General Psychiatry 32:285–305.

Angst J, ed (1983) The origins of depressions: Current concepts and approaches. Springer, Berlin / Heidelberg / New York.

Angst J, Isele R, Scharfetter C, Scheidegger P (1985) Zur prämorbiden Persönlichkeit Schizophrener. Schweizer Archiv fur Neurologie, Neurochirurgie und Psychiatrie 136:45–53.

Backus W, Chapian M (1980) Befreiende Wahrheit: Praxis kognitiver Seelsorge. Projektion J, Hochheim 1983.

Baker D, Nester E (1983) Zurück ins Leben. Die Geschichte einer Depression. Brunnen-Verlag, Basel/Gießen 1986.

Battegay R (1985) Depression: psychophysische und soziale Dimension. Therapie. Huber, Bern / Stuttgart / Toronto.

Beck AT (1981) Kognitive Therapie der Depression. Urban und Schwarzenberg, München / Wien / Baltimore.

Becker W (1982) Wahrnehmungen. Wie wir uns und andere neu sehen lernen. Oncken, Wuppertal/Kassel.

Begley S, Carey J, Sawhill R (1983) How the brain works. Newsweek 7. Februar, S. 40–47.

Benedetti G (1960) Blumhardts Seelsorge in der Sicht heutiger psychotherapeutischer Kenntnis. Reformatio 9:474–487 (1. Teil) und 531–539 (2. Teil).

Bennett Ml, Bennett MB (1984) The uses of hopelessness. American Journal of Psychiatry 141:559—562.

Black DA (1984) Paulus Infirmus: The pauline concept of weakness. Grace Theological Journal 5:77–93.

Blackburn B (1986) Was Sie über Selbstmord wissen sollten. Blaukreuz-Verlag Wuppertal / Bern.

Blankenburg W und Zilly A (1973) Gestaltwandel im schizophrenen Wahnerleben? In Glatzel J, Hg.: Gestaltwandel psychiatrischer Krankheitsbilder. Schattauer, Stuttgart.

Bleuler E (1975) Lehrbuch der Psychiatrie. 13.Auflage. Springer, Berlin/Heidelberg / New York.

Blumhardt JC (1968) Seelsorge. Siebenstern Taschenbuch Verlag, Hamburg / München.

Böker W und Brenner HD, Hg. (1986) Bewältigung der Schizophrenie. Huber, Bern / Stuttgart / Toronto.

Bräutigam W und Christian P (1981) Psychosomatische Medizin. Ein kurzgefasstes Lehrbuch. Thieme Verlag, Stuttgart / New York.

Braun P et al. (1981) Overview: Deinstitutionalization of psychiatric patients, a critical review of outcome studies. American Journal of Psychiatry 138:736–749.

Bronisch T (1987) Rehabilitation chronifizierter Neurosen. Vortrag gehalten am Internationalen Symposium über Rehabilitation in der Psychiatrie in München. 8.-10.4.1987.

Bufford RK, Johnston TB (1982) The church and community mental health: unrealized potential. Journal of Psychology and Theology 10:355–362.

Cartwright R (1978) Schlafen und Träumen. Eine Einführung in die experimentelle Schlafforschung. Kindler, München 1982.

Ciompi L (1981) Wie können wir die Schizophrenen besser verstehen? - Eine Synthese neuer Krankheits- und Therapiekonzepte. Der Nervenarzt 52:506–515.

Coenen L, Beyreuther E und Bietenhard H, Hg. (1983) Theologisches Begriffslexikon zum Neuen Testament,

Band 1 und 2. R. Brockhaus, Wuppertal.

Collins G (1979) Einführung in die beratende Seelsorge. Bundes-Verlag, Witten.

Collins G (1985) The magnificent mind. Waco TX: Word.

Cosgrove MP (1977) The essence of human nature. Christian free university curriculum. Zondervan, Grand Rapids Ml.

Cosgrove MP (1979) Psychology gone awry. Intervarsity Press. Downers Grove (ILL).

Crabb LJ (1984) Die Last des andern: Biblische Seelsorge als Aufgabe der Gemeinde. Brunnen-Verlag, Basel/Giessen.

Der Spiegel (1978), 'Schizophrenie austragen wie einen Schnupfen': In Italien werden die Irrenanstalten durch Gesetz abgeschafft. 47:195–207.

Der Spiegel (1983) Schande ohne Ende. 44:271–275.

Dethlefsen T (1976) Das Erlebnis der Wiedergeburt. Heilung durch Reinkarnation. Bertelsmann Verlag, München.

Dieterich M (1984) Psychologie contra Seelsorge? Hänssler, Neuhausen-Stuttgart.

Dieterich M (1986) Depressionen. Hilfen aus biblischer und psychotherapeutischer Sicht. Brunnen-Verlag, Basel/Giessen.

Dilling H (1981) Prävalenzergebnisse aus einer Feldstudie in einem ländlich-kleinstädtischen Gebiet. In: Mester H, Tölle R: Neurosen. Springer, Berlin / Heidelberg / New York.

Dörner K, Egetmeyer A, Koenning K (1982) Freispruch der Familie. Psychiatrie Verlag, Wunstorff/ Hannover.

Drake RE, Sederer Ll (1986) Inpatient psychosocial treatment of chronic schizophrenia: negative effects and current guidelines. Hospital and Community Psychiatry 37:897–901.

Eccles JC (1979) Das menschliche Gehirn. Piper, München.

Egan G (1984) Helfen durch Gespräch. Psychologische Beratung in Therapie, Beruf und Alltag. Rowohlt, Reinbek.

Ellis A (1977) Die rational-emotive Therapie: das innere Selbstgespräch bei seelischen Problemen und seine

Veränderung. Pfeiffer Verlag, München.

Ernst C, Von Luckner N (1985) Stellt die Frühkindheit die Weichen? Eine Kritik an der Lehre von der schicksalhaften Bedeutung erster Erlebnisse. Enke Verlag, Stuttgart.

Ernst K (1981) Praktische Klinikpsychiatrie für Ärzte und Pflegepersonal. Springer, Berlin / Heidelberg / New York.

Ernst K (1984) Ideen und Tatsachen in der Psychiatrie. Ursachen und Folgen einer vernachlässigten Unterscheidung. Tages-Anzeiger 6.Juli 1984, S.49.

Ernst K (1986) Psychiatrische Versorgung: Das humane Minimum und seine Kosten. In: Heimann H und Gaertner HJ, Hg.: Das Verhältnis der Psychiatrie zu ihren Nachbardisziplinen. Springer, Berlin/Heidelberg/New York.

Ernst K, Ernst C (1986) Italienische Psychiatrie: Augenschein in der Lombardei. Der Nervenarzt 57:494–501.

Eschenrödter CT (1984) Hier irrte Freud. Urban und Schwarzenberg, München / Wien / Baltimore.

Eysenck HJ, Kamin L (1981) The intelligence controversy. John Wiley, New York / Toronto.

Farah C (1984) Von der Zinne des Tempels. Glaube oder Vermessenheit? Fliss-Verlag, Hamburg.

Feldmann H (1984) Psychiatrie und Psychotherapie. Ein kurzgefasstes Lehrbuch für Studierende und Ärzte. Karger, Basel / München.

Fester als Felsen. Schulte und Gerth, Asslar 1984.

Fiedler P, Niedermeier T, Mundt C (1986) Gruppenarbeit mit Angehörigen schizophrener Patienten. Psychologie Verlags Union, München/Weinheim.

Flach F (1978) Depression als Lebenschance. Seelische Krisen und wie man sie nutzt. Rowohlt, Reinbek.

Frankl V (1983) Ärztliche Seelsorge: Grundlagen der Logotherapie und Existenzanalyse. Fischer Taschenbuch Verlag, Frankfurt.

Freud A (1984) Das Ich und die Abwehrmechanismen.

Fischer Taschenbuch Verlag, Frankfurt.

Garcia C und Sander HJ (1983) Pseudohysterische Verhaltensweisen bei endogenen Depressionen. Der Nervenarzt 54:354–362.

Gassmann L (1984) Gruppendynamik—Hintergründe und Beurteilung. Hänssler, Neuhausen-Stuttgart.

GEO-Wissen (1987) Gehirn, Gefuhl, Gedanken. Nr.l, 25. Mai.

Gmür M (1986) Die Fragwurdigkeit des Borderline-Begriffs. Schweizerische Ärztezeitung 67:2219–2221.

Green H (1978) Ich hab dir nie einen Rosengarten versprochen. Bericht einer Heilung. Rowohlt, Reinbek.

Grove WM, Andreasen NC (1985) Language and Thinking in Psychosis. Archives of General Psychiatry 42:26–32.

Gunderson JG et al. (1984) Effects of psychotherapy in schizophrenia 11:comparative outcome of two forms of treatment. Schizophrenia Bulletin 10:564–598.

Haefely W, Möhler H (1980) Der Wirkungsmechanismus der Benzodiazepine. Ein Bericht aus der Roche-Forschung. Hoffmann-La Roche, Basel.

Häfner H (1985) Sind psychische Krankheiten häufiger geworden? Der Nervenarzt 56:120– 133.

Haenel T (1983) Aberglaube, Glaube, Wahn. Schweizer Archiv für Neurologie, Neurochirurgie und Psychiatrie 133:295–310.

Haller M (1983) Neuer Psychokult: Lust aufs Jenseits. Der Spiegel 43:268–279.

Hampden-Turner C (1982) Modelle des Menschen. Beltz, Weinheim/Basel.

Hark H (1984) Religiöse Neurosen: Ursache und Heilung. Kreuz Verlag, Stuttgart.

Hartmann E, Milofsky E, Vaillant G et al. (1984) Vulnerability to schizophrenia. Archives of General Psychiatry 41:1050–1056.

Heinrich K (1983) Psychopharmaka in Klinik und Praxis. Thieme Verlag, Stuttgart / New York.

Hell D (1987) Angehörigenarbeit in der Psychiatrie. Praxis der Psychotherapie und Psychosomatik 32:87–94.

Hemminger H (1982) Kindheit als Schicksal? Die Frage nach den Langzeitfolgen frühkindlicher seelischer Verletzungen. Rowohlt, Reinbek.

Hemminger H (1987) Psychotherapie-Weg zum Glück? Zur Orientierung auf dem Psychomarkt. Verlag: Evangelischer Presseverband für Bayern, München.

Hemminger H, Becker V (1985) Wenn Therapien schaden: Kritische Analyse einer psychotherapeutischen Fallgeschichte. Rowohlt, Reinbek.

Hennenhofer G, Heil KD (1979) Angst überwinden: Selbstbefreiung durch Verhaltenstraining. Rowohlt, Reinbek.

Holaday JW (1984) Endogenous opioid systems and autonomic function. Clinical Neuropharmacology Vol. 7, Suppl. 1, Raven Press, New York, 726–727.

Hole G (1977) Der Glaube bei Depressiven. Enke Verlag, Stuttgart.

Horie M (1978) Resignieren oder hoffen? Ein Leitfaden für Seelsorger. R.Brockhaus, Wuppertal.

Horie M, Horie H (1985) Stufen der Befreiung. Scheitern und Neubeginn. R.Brockhaus, Wuppertal.

Huber G (1983) Das Konzept substratnaher Basissymptome und seine Bedeutung für Theorie und Therapie schizophrener Erkrankungen. Der Nervenarzt 54:23–32.

Huth W (1984) Glaube, Ideologie und Wahn: Das Ich zwischen Realität und Illusion. Nymphenburger, München.

Jaeggi Eva (1986) Pop-Psychologie: Abkürzungen zum Ich? Psychologie heute 10, S. 62–67.

Jaspers K (1959) General Psychopathology. Springer, Berlin/Heidelberg / New York.

Jones DG (1981) Our fragile brains: a christian perspective on brain research. Intervarsity Press. Downers Grove (ILL).

Kagan J (1987) Die Natur des Kindes. Piper, München.

Keller MB, Lavori PW, RiceJ et al. (1986) The persistent risk of chonicity in recurrent episodes of nonbipolar major depressive disorder: a prospective follow-up. American Journal of Psychiatry 143:24–28.

Kielholz P (1974) Diagnose und Therapie der Depressionen für den Praktiker. Lehmanns, München.

Kielholz P (1981) Diagnostik larvierter Depressionen. In: Kielholz P und Pöldinger W (Hg): Der depressive Patient und sein Arzt. Springer, Berlin / Heidelberg / New York.

Kielholz P, Adams C (1984) Vermeidbare Fehler in Diagnostik und Therapie der Depression. Deutscher Ärzte-Verlag, Köln.

Kielholz P, Poeldinger W und Adams C (1981) Die larvierte Depression. Deutscher Ärzte-Verlag, Köln.

Kind H (1982) Psychotherapie und Psychotherapeuten: Methoden und Praxis. Thieme Verlag, Stuttgart / New York.

Knoll J (1984) Endogenous anorexic substances. Clinical Neuropharmacology Vol 7, Suppl 1, Raven Press, New York, 724–725.

Koch ER (1978) Chirurgie der Seele: Operative Umpolung des Verhaltens. Fischer Verlag, Frankfurt.

Köhler A (1978) Religiöser Wahn und Religiosität. Dissertation, Universität Zürich.

König R (1986) New Age: Geheime Gehirnwäsche. Wie man uns heute für morgen programmiert. Hänssler, Neuhausen-Stuttgart.

Koenigsberg HW, Handley R (1986) Expressed emotion: from predictive index to clinical construct. American Joumal of Psychiatry 143: 1361–1373.

Kranz H (1955) Das Thema des Wahns im Wandel der Zeit. Fortschritte der Neurologie und Psychiatrie 23:58–72.

Kranz H (1967) Wahn und Zeitgeist. Studium Generale, 20:605–611 .

Küng H (1987) Freud und die Zukunft der Religion. Piper, München.

Lasch C (1986) Das Zeitalter des NarziBmus. Deutscher Taschenbuch Verlag, München.

Lausch E (1974) Manipulation—Der Griff nach dem Gehirn. Rowohlt, Reinbek.

Laux G (1986) Chronifizierte Depressionen. Eine klinische Verlaufsuntersuchung unter Berücksichtigung typologischer, therapeutischer und prognostischer Aspekte. Enke Verlag, Stuttgart.

Lazarus A, Fay A (1985) Ich kann, wenn ich will. Deutscher Taschenbuch Verlag, München.

Lechler A (1978) Krankheit oder Dämonie? Verlag Goldene Worte, Stuttgart.

Lewis CS (1980) Wunder: möglich, wahrscheinlich, undenkbar? Brunnen-Verlag, Basel / Giessen.

Mader A (1978) Der angenommene Mensch. Gedanken eines Nervenarztes. R. Brockhaus, Wuppertal.

Margies W (1983) Heilung durch sein Wort: Der Verzicht auf Psychotherapie. Teil 1 und 2, STIWA Druck und Verlag, Urbach, 4. Auflage.

Marks J (1985) Chronic anxiolytic treatment: benefit and risk. In: Kemali D and Racagni G, eds, Chronic treatments in neuropsychiatry. Raven Press, New York Maslow AH (1968) Psychologie des Seins. Kindler, München.

Mauz G (1986) . . . 'nur demutiges Schweigen angemessen' Der Spiegel 32:80–81.

Maymann U (1984) Die religiöse Welt psychisch Kranker. Ein Beitrag zur Kranken seelsorge. Herder, Freiburg / Basel / Wien.

McClung F (1985) The Father Heart of God. Kingsway Publications, Eastbourne.

McFarlane JW (1964) Perspectives on personality consistency and change from the guidance study. Vita humana 7:115–126.

Mester H und Tölle R (1981) Neurosen. Springer, Berlin/Heidelberg/New York.

Michel KM (1985) Im Bauch des Wals: Abgesang auf die gesunde Persönlichkeit. In: Michel KM, Spengler T, Hg.:

Die Therapiegesellschaft. Kursbuch 82, Berlin.

Miller A (1983) Das Drama des begabten Kindes und die Suche nach dem wahren Selbst. Suhrkamp Verlag, Frankfurt/ Berlin.

Müller C (1985) ber späte Besserungen bei chronischen Schizophrenen. Schweizer Archiv für Neurologie, Neurochirurgie und Psychiatrie 136:17–22.

Müller L (1984) Die Wiederkehr des Magischen. Psychologie heute, September, S. 21–27.

Müller P, Günther U, LohmeyerJ (1986) Behandlung und Verlauf schizophrener Psychosen über ein Jahrzehnt. Krankheitsverlauf und Prädiktoren. Der Nervenarzt 57:332–341.

Needham 1(1988) Pflegeplanung in der Psychiatrie. Recom, Basel.

Neidhart J (1985) Leib, Seele und Geist. Dichotomie oder Trichotomie? Bibel und Gemeinde 3:281–299.

Nohl PG (1981) Mit seelischer Krankheit leben. Hilfen für Betroffene und Mitbetroffene. Vandenhoeck & Ruprecht, Göttingen.

Nuechterlein KH, Dawson ME (1984) Information processing and attentional functioning in the developmental course of schizophrenic disorders. Schizophrenia Bulletin 10/ 2:160–203.

Oates WE (1980) Seelsorge und Psychiatrie. Styria Verlag, Graz/Wien/Köln.

Obiols J, Basaglia F (1978) Antipsychiatrie: Das neue Verständnis psychischer Krankheit. Rowohlt, Reinbek.

Oden TC (1974) Wer sagt: Du bist okay? Eine theologische Anfrage an die Transaktionale Analyse. BCS Burkardthaus, Berlin 1977.

Papeschi R (1985) The denial of the institution: a critical review of Franco Basaglia's writings. British Journal of Psychiatry 146:247–254.

Pardes H (1986) Neuroscience and Psychiatry: Marriage or Coexistence? American Journal of Psychiatry 143:1205–1212.

Perry JC, Klerman GL (1978). The borderline Patient. American Journal of Psychiatry 35:141–150.

Pfeifer S (1985) Therapeuteneigenschaften und Erfolg in der Psychotherapie. Schweizerische Ärztezeitung 66:1534–1539.

Pfeifer S (1987) Okkulte Belastung im Spannungsfeld von Seelsorge und Psychiatrie. Factum, Februarheft, 3–8.

Phelps M, Mazziotta J (1985) Positron emission tomography: human brain function and biochemistry. Science 228:799–809.

Poeldinger W (1982/1) Die psychiatrische Klinik im Wandel. Schweizerische Ärztezeitung 63:285–288.

Poeldinger W (1982/2) Erkennung und Beurteilung der Suizidalität. In: Reimer C, Hg.: Suizid. Springer, Berlin / Heidelberg / New York 1982.

Poeldinger W (1984) Über systemisches und perspektivisches Denken in der Psychiatrie. Schweizerische Ärztezeitung 65:1573–1574.

Poeldinger W, Wider F (1986) Die Therapie der Depressionen. Deutscher Ärzte-Verlag, Köln.

Pribham KH (1986) The cognitive revolution and mind / brain issues. American Psychologist 41:507–520.

Rainer JD (1980) Genetics and Psychiatry. In: Comprehensive textbook of psychiatry, 3rd ed. Edited by Kaplan Hl, Freedman AM, Saddock BJ. Williams & Wilkins, Baltimore/London, S.135–154.

Reimer C, Hg (1982) Suizid. Springer, Berlin/Heidelberg/ New York.

Restack RM (1985) Geheimnisse des menschlichen Gehirns. Ursprung von Denken, Fühlen, Handeln. Moderne Verlagsgesellschaft, Landsberg am Lech.

Rickels K, Case WG, Downing RW, Winokur A (1985) Indications and contraindications for chronic anxiolytic treatment: is there tolerance to the anxiolytic effect? In: Kemali D and Racagni G, eds, Chronic treatments in neuropsychiatry. Raven Press, New York.

Riemann F (1975) Grundformen der Angst. Eine tiefenpsychologische Studie. Ernst Reinhardt Verlag, München.

Rogers CR (1977) Die Kraft des Guten: Ein Appell zur Selbstverwirklichung. Fischer Verlag, Frankfurt 1985.

Rogers CR (1983) Therapeut und Klient: Grundlagen der Gesprächspsychotherapie. Fischer Verlag, Frankfurt.

Rohner HK (1985) Transpersonale Psychologie stösst in höhere Sphären vor. Tages-Anzeiger 4. April.

Rosenhan DL (1973) On being sane in insane places. Science 179:250–258.

Roy-Byrne PP, Geraci M, Uhde TW (1986) Life events and the onset of panic disorder. American Journal of Psychiatry 143:1424–1427.

Ruppert HJ (1985) New Age: Endzeit oder Wendezeit? Coprint, Wiesbaden.

Sass H, Koehler K (1983) Borderline-Syndrome: Grenzgebiet oder Niemandsland? Zur klinisch-psychiatrischen Relevanz von Borderline-Diagnosen. Der Nervenarzt 54:221–230.

Sass H, Köhler K (1984) Diagnostisches und Statistisches Manual psychischer Störungen (DSM 111). Beltz-Verlag, Weinheim/Basel.

Schaeffer E (1986) Nie tiefer als in Gottes Hand. Hänssler, Neuhausen-Stuttgart.

Scharfetter C (1986) Schizophrene Menschen. Psychologie Verlags Union, München / Weinheim .

Scharrer E (1984) Psychisches Fehlverhalten und die Heilung der Gottesbeziehung. Francke, Marburg.

Schepank (1974) Erb- und Umweltfaktoren bei Neurosen. Springer, Berlin / Heidelberg / New York.

Scherer K (1982) Vergebung-das zentrale Problem. Hänssler, Neuhausen-Stuttgart.

Schmidbauer W (1977) Die hilflosen Helfer. Rowohlt, Reinbek.

Schmidbauer W (1983) Helfen als Beruf: Die Ware Nächstenliebe. Rowohlt, Reinbek.

Schou M (1978) Lithium-Behandlung der manisch-depressiven Krankheit. Information für Arzt und Patienten. Thieme Verlag, Stuttgart/New York 1980.

Searle JR (1984) Minds, brains and science. Harvard University Press, Cambridge MA.

Sedvall G, Farde L, Persson A und Wiesel FA (1986) Imaging of Neurotransmitter Receptors in the living human brain. Archives of General Psychiatry 43:995–1005.

Silverman JS, Silverman JA, Eardley DA (1984) Do Maladaptive Attitudes Cause Depression? Arch Gen Psychiatry 41:28–30.

Simons AD, Garfield SL, Murphy GE (1984) The Process of Change in Cognitive Therapy and Pharmacotherapy for Depression. Arch Gen Psychiatry 41:45–51.

Smedes LB (1984) Forgive and forget. Harper & Row, San Francisco.

Stoop D (1982) Self talk: key to personal growth. Revell, Old Tappan NJ.

Strauch P (1982) Entdeckungen in der Einsamkeit. Bundes-Verlag, Witten.

Strupp HH, Hadley SW (1977) A tripartite model of mental health and therapeutic outcomes. With special reference to negative effects in psychotherapy. American Psychologist 32:187–196.

Süllwold L (1977) Symptome schizophrener Erkrankungen. Uncharakteristische Basisstörungen. Springer, Berlin/Heidelberg/ New York.

Süllwold L, Huber G (1986) Schizophrene Basisstörungen. Springer, Berlin/Heidelberg/New York.

Szasz TS (1972) Geisteskrankheit-ein moderner Mythos? Grundzüge einer Theorie des persönlichen Verhaltens. Walter Verlag, Olten/Freiburg.

Szasz TS (1975) Psychiatrie- die verschleierte Macht. Walter Verlag, Olten / Freiburg.

Tan SY (1987) Cognitive-behavior therapy: A biblical approach and critique.Journal of Psychology and Theology 15:103–112

Thurneysen E (1980) Die Lehre von der Seelsorge. Theologischer Verlag Zürich, Zürich (Erstausgabe 1946).

Tölle R (1982) Lehrbuch der Psychiatrie. Springer, Berlin/Heidelberg/New York.

Tölle R, Peikert A, Rieke A (1987) Persönlichkeitsstörungen bei Melancholiekranken. Der Nervenarzt 58:227–236.

Tournier P (ohneJg) Echte und falsche Schuldgefühle: Vom schlechten Gewissen zur inneren Freiheit. 6. Auflage. Humata Verlag Pforzheim/Bern / Salzburg.

Vanauken S, Lewis CS (1980) Eine harte Gnade. Brunnen-Verlag, Giessen/Basel.

Van Hout L, Hg. (1988) Rehabilitation in der Psychiatrie. Springer, Berlin/Heidelberg/New York.

VonOrelli A (1954) Der Wandel des Inhaltes der depressiven Ideen bei der reinen Melancholie. Schweizer Archiv fur Neurologie, Neurochirurgie und Psychiatrie 73:217–287.

Walsh RN und Vaughan F, Hg. (1980) Psychologie in der Wende. Scherz, Bern/München/Wien, 2.dt.Auflage 1985.

Watson D (1984) Fear no evil. Hodder & Stoughton, London.

Weiner H (1980) Schizophrenia: Etiology. In: Comprehensive textbook of psychiatry, 3rd ed. Edited by Kaplan Hl, Freedman AM, Saddock BJ. Baltimore, Williams & Wilkins, S. 1121–1152.

Weyerer S, Dilling H (1984) Prävalenz und Behandlung psychischer Erkrankungen in der Allgemeinbevölkerung. Ergebnisse einer Feldstudie in drei Gemeinden Oberbayerns. Der Nervenarzt 55:30–42.

WhiteJ (1987) Die Masken der Melancholie. Francke, Marburg.

Will H (1985) Selige Gesundheit: Systeme der Therapiegesellschaft. In: Michel K M, Spengler T, Hg.: Die Therapiegesellschaft. Kursbuch 82, Berlin.

Willi J (1985) Koevolution: Die Kunst gemeinsamen Wachsens. Rowohlt, Reinbek.

WilliamsJMG (1984) Cognitive-Behaviour Therapy for Depression: Problems and Perspectives. BritJ Psychiatry 145:254–262.

Wright HN (1981) Marital counseling: A biblically based behavioral approach. Harper & Row, New York.

Yancey P (1979) Schmerz- Hat Gott denn kein Mitleid? Schulte und Gerth, Asslar.

Zilbergeld B (1983) The Shrinking of America: Myths of Psychological Change. Little, Brown, Boston/Toronto.

Zubin J und Spring B (1977) Vulnerability: a new view of schizophrenia. Journal of Abnormal Psychology 86:103–123.

Zubin J, Magaziner J und Steinhauer S (1983) The metamorphosis of schizophrenia from chronicity to vulnerability. Psychosocial Medicine 13:551–571.

Zweifel A, Scharfetter C (1977) Christliche Religiosität und Psychosethematik. Schweizer Archiv fur Neurologie, Neurochirurgie und Psychiatrie 121:317–324.

INDEX

Addiction   21, 86, 88, 142, 172f., 192

Aggression   45, 75, 132

Alcohol   88, 133

Alzheimer's Disease   59

Analytic—dynamic model   31ff

Anger   16, 35, 64, 92

Antidepressants   50, 128ff., 183, 191

Anxiety   31ff., 49ff., 60ff., 73., 85ff., 103, 119ff., 152, 156ff., 185ff., 191, 198, 201, 205

Anxiety neurosis   74ff.

Autonomic nervous system   50f., 60, 74f., 82, 101

Belief system   67ff.

Behavioural Therapy   30, 32ff., 37, 161

Behaviour Therapy -
  moralistic model   30, 32f.

Bible   15., 19, 27, 33, 36ff., 61ff., 66ff., 88, 93ff., 124ff., 159ff., 169ff., 179ff., 197ff.

Biochemistry   49, 69, 88, 101, 113f., 123, 128, 149, 152, 164, 194

Birth trauma   58ff., 62

Body Language   49

Brain   20, 41ff., 58ff., 69, 88, 90, 113f., 123, 128f, 149, 152, 164, 194, 201

Brain damage | 17, 40, 43, 46, 54, 59f., 80, 111, 112f, 150

Brain, organic disorders of | 10f, 17, 43, 46, 59, 69, 90, 113f., 140, 149, 152, 187

Brain surgery | 46

Catatonic state | 143f.

Childhood | 16, 31ff., 57, 62ff., 75, 80, 111, 113, 134, 180

Chronic Depression | 78, 112, 116f.

Chronic Schizophrenia | 150

Co-operation between doctor and pastoral counsellor | 9, 18, 27, 101, 174, 175, 183, 185, 197, 200

Compassion | 36, 50, 88, 98, 161, 163, 173, 181, 186, 193f

Compulsion | 73ff., 77, 80, 82, 85, 89ff., 94, 98, 134, 197

Continued medication | 164

Conversational ability | 166, 185

Creation | 75, 102f., 114, 129

Criticism of Psychiatry | 22

Daily Routine | 128f, 166f

Damage to the brain | (See brain damage)

Dementia in old age | 43, 140

Demons | 8, 38, 50, 86, 94, 131ff., 157ff., 187

Depression | 16f., 23, 50, 59f., 64, 69, 74, 82, 99ff., 123ff., 188

Depression, bipolar | 117, 140

Depression, causes | 111ff.

Depression, chronic | 79, 117f.

Depression, diagnosis | 101ff., 104

Depression, monopolar | 111f., 117

Depression, neurotic | 74, 82, 92, 111f.

Depression, organic | 111f.

Depression, pastoral care of	69, 99, 101ff., 111, 119, 123ff., 181ff., 188ff., 201
Depression, reactive	75f., 93, 111f.
Depression, treatment	50, 101, 123ff., 186ff.
Depth Psychology	31ff., 40, 63
Diagnosis	7, 11f., 20f., 23, 76f., 82, 101f., 111, 142f., 180f.
Disorders of adaptability	20, 80
Disposition	55ff., 63ff., 80, 112f., 180
Doubt	16, 29, 98, 99, 187
E.E.G.	47
Excessive demands	8f., 25f., 33, 75, 125ff., 135f., 152, 166, 174f., 188f.
Faith healing	195, 198f.
Forgiveness	10f., 32, 98, 155, 182
Genetic inheritance	59f., 80, 141, 150f., 162
God, understanding of	104
Grieving Process	195ff.
Group therapies	35f., 167
Guilt	62, 90, 95, 102ff., 119f., 125, 133, 152, 161, 182, 196
Hebephrenia	144
Helper syndrome	22
Hepatitis	111
Hope	23f., 66, 69, 100, 115, 121, 123, 134, 171, 173, 179, 198, 200, 204ff.
Hormones	51, 49
Hospital	22ff., 42, 77, 135f., 141, 147, 158, 165f., 169ff., 190ff., 195ff.
Human nature, image of	29ff., 50f.
Humanistic relationship orientated model	30, 34ff.

Hypnosis	38
Hypothalamus	46, 49
Hysteria	75, 80, 82, 85, 92ff.
Increase of psychiatric disorders	7, 17
Information, processing	41ff., 47, 51, 90, 149, 152f.
Inner healing	32, 88, 181, 182, 204
Integration of psychiatry & pastoral counselling	8, 36ff., 179ff.
Intelligence	60f.
Intermittent course (in phases)	78f., 120, 125, 137, 142f., 146, 165, 166ff.
Isolation	7, 86, 95, 117, 134
Limitations	36, 63, 78, 87, 88, 91ff., 162, 165, 181, 195ff.
Lithium	130
Long term prognosis	18
Mania	7, 26, 116, 117f., 119ff., 129, 140, 143f., 146, 152f., 156, 165, 171, 181, 191
Medication	20, 23, 42, 86ff., 91, 100, 147f., 162, 165f., 170ff., 180, 183, 186, 180ff., 205
Meditation	37f.
Miracles	198ff.
Multi-dimensional perspective	179f.
Mystic - occult model	30, 37ff.
Narcissism	35
Neuroleptic drugs	166, 172f., 182, 191f.
Neuroses	17, 21, 73ff., 85ff.
Neuroses, causes of	79ff.
Neuroses, course of	78f.
Neuroses, diagnosis	82ff.
Neuroses, forms of	76ff., 85ff.
Neuroses, pastoral care	88, 90ff.
Neuroses, treatment of	87f., 91f., 95f.

Neurosis, religious (ecclesiogenic) 8, 95
Neurotransmitter 48ff.
New Age Movement 37
Occult 37f., 161
Occult Bondage 37, 38, 94, 161f., 171, 187, 196
Organic illnesses (See also organic brain disorders) 43ff., 110, 140
Oversensitivity (See also vulnerability) 64, 113, 150ff.
Panic 86
Pastoral Counselling 8ff., 18, 21ff., 26f., 31, 32f., 36f., 39f., 43, 50, 58, 61, 66, 77, 83, 87, 91ff., 95ff., 99, 100, 104, 114, 118f., 184f., 200
Patience 32, 62, 66, 98, 118, 124f., 137, 171, 173, 181f., 185, 197ff.
Personality 45ff., 53, 61, 130, 140, 159
Personality disorders 17, 20, 76ff., 85, 140, 143, 147, 155, 191, 205
Physical problems 59f., 64, 67, 75, 82, 86, 103f., 112, 113, 114, 123, 172
Practical help 124, 127, 130, 172, 183f., 188ff., 207
Prayer 66, 93ff., 104, 171, 186f., 206
Psychoanalysis 31ff., 43
Psycho-organic syndrome 140
Psychoboom 20
Psychogenic disorder 77, 110
Psychopharmacy (See medication)

Psychoses	10, 17, 21, 93, 116, 128ff., 139ff., 155ff., 165ff., 186f., 192
Psychosomatic	17, 50f., 64, 74ff., 110
Psychotherapy	8ff., 16, 18ff., 29ff., 55, 66, 79, 88, 91, 94, 163, 200
Relationships, absence of	7, 34, 76, 79, 92
Relatives	24f., 83, 89, 120f., 127, 134ff., 141, 148, 151, 161, 163ff., 188ff., 190, 196ff.
Relaxation	49, 88f.
Religiosity	8ff., 25f., 38, 94, 143, 155ff., 171f.
Repression of religion	8, 25
Residual phase in neuroses	77ff.
Residual phase in Schizphrenia	144ff., 166, 172
Resources	11, 57, 188f.
Responsibility	33, 35, 86, 136, 160f., 165
Restrictions	16, 74, 76f., 82, 182
Schizoaffective psychosis	111, 144
Schizophrenia	10ff., 17, 139ff., 150, 155ff., 175ff., 185
Schizophrenia and faith	155ff., 165ff.
Schizophrenia and pastoral care	69, 159ff., 186
Schizophrenia and Psychotherapy	168
Schizophrenia and sin	160f.
Schizophrenia and the Occult	161ff.
Schizophrenia simplex	144
Schizophrenia, catatonic form	144
Schizophrenia, Chronic	150
Schizophrenia, Course of	142ff., 150
Schizophrenia, diagnosis	142ff.
Schizophrenia, forms of	111, 144ff.
Schizophrenia, Hebephrenic form	144

Schizophrenia, hereditary factors 141
Schizophrenia, origin 50, 150ff.
Schizophrenia, paranoid form 145
Schizophrenia, pastoral care of 155, 166ff.
Schizophrenia, Phases of 142f., 166f.
Schizophrenia simplex 144
Schizophrenia, Therapy 26, 165ff., 186ff.
Self-realisation 35ff.
Side effects 130f., 166, 173
Sin 34, 36, 73, 90, 98, 99, 111, 118f., 126, 155, 157, 160ff., 171, 182
Sleep 16, 49, 58f., 64f., 75, 102ff., 107f., 116, 144, 173, 192f.
Slight disorders 16ff., 23f., 31, 55ff., 77, 81f., 100f., 104, 114, 119, 125, 128, 140, 165, 182, 186f.
Stress 49, 56, 64ff., 113f., 123, 150ff., 167
Substitute religion 18f., 37f.
Suicide 26, 102f., 106, 131ff., 168
Symptoms, fluctuation of 77f.
Talking 18f., 23, 31, 34, 36, 91f., 96, 123ff., 131, 134ff., 165ff., 173, 183ff., 188, 198f.
Temperament 58, 60ff.
Therapeutic society 16
Thought 20, 33f., 44, 52, 56, 60, 64ff., 74f., 85f., 90f., 115, 116, 120, 123f., 126f., 131ff., 140f., 143, 148f., 149, 152, 168, 180
Thought, models of 19, 30

Tranquilisers	16, 49f., 88, 91, 130, 135, 166
Transpersonal Psychology	37f.
Trauma, childhood	17, 31f., 62, 80
Upbringing	31f., 60f., 63, 95, 158
Weakness	9ff., 15, 33, 56ff., 64, 66, 76, 92ff., 150, 171f., 175, 180ff., 182ff., 201f., 205ff.
Work	45, 59f., 75, 79, 86, 89f., 100, 140, 143, 150, 156, 159, 172f., 188f., 191f.
World view	8f., 37, 39, 158f.

HEALING AT ANY PRICE?

Samuel Pfeifer M.D.

'. . . destined to become one of the most informative books on the subject of alternative medicine that has ever been written.'

From the Foreword by Selwyn Hughes

Many people, feeling increasingly alienated from modern technological medicine, have turned to alternative remedies. But what are their underlying philosophies? Following extensive research, Dr Pfeifer discusses various branches of New Age medicine, including acupuncture, homoeopathy, iridology and radiesthesia. He looks at the beliefs of those who pioneered their use, and concludes that some have their roots in Eastern philosophy and occult practices. Dr Pfeifer estimates the success of each of these methods, and suggests possible reasons for their effectiveness.

Catalogue Number YB 9153   £2.95